nine elements

of a successful safety & health system

John Czerniak, CSP & Don Ostrander, CSP

Cover and interior design: Dawn Pope

NATIONAL SAFETY COUNCIL MISSION STATEMENT

The mission of the National Safety Council is to educate and influence society to adopt safety, health, and environmental policies, practices, and procedures that prevent and mitigate human suffering and economic losses arising from preventable causes.

COPYRIGHT, WAIVER OF FIRST SALE DOCTRINE

DISCLAIMER

Copyright © 2005 by the National Safety Council

All Rights Reserved

Printed in the United States of America

32 31 30 29 28 27 26

Czerniak, John, 1956-

  Nine elements of a successful safety & health system / John Czerniak,

Don Ostrander.

    p. cm.

  Includes index.

  ISBN 978-0-87912-257-7

  1. Industrial safety--United States--Management. 2. Industrial

hygiene--United States--Management. 3. Work environment--United States.

I. Ostrander, Don, 1949- II. Title.

  T55.C94 2005

  658.3'82--dc22

                                                                        2005005563

2C05192022   NSC Product: 121840000   ISBN: 978-0-87912-257-7

authors

John A. Czerniak, CSP, MBA, has a diverse background in regulation and safety, health and environmental management. He has been successful in guiding senior plant management and employee leadership teams in active development of site specific safety management systems that significantly reduced employee injuries. As a senior consultant at the National Safety Council, he is responsible for field consulting and training services and maintaining knowledge of significant trends.

Don M. Ostrander, CSP, has 28 years of experience as a safety manager, consultant, trainer and project manager. He has a proven track record of expertise and leadership in safety management both on and off the shop floor. As Director of Product Development and Project Manager of Occupational Safety and Health Services for the National Safety Council, he is responsible for development, implementation and management of occupational products and services and consulting projects.

contents

introduction

A safety management system is a core element of an organization that effectively protects the health and safety of its employees. It is a systematic process that holds management accountable for managing safety through goal setting, defining roles and responsibilities, developing proactive performance measures and holding individuals accountable for their responsibilities within the management system. Success or failure to achieve goals within the system is treated in the same manner as success or failure to achieve production goals, quality goals, or sales or budget goals. The safety management system is a continuous management process that, through time, reduces hazards and prevents incidents. Safety management systems are integrated into every-day processes throughout the organization all year.

Safety management systems differ from traditional safety programs in many ways. In a traditional safety program, management decides the injury rate is too high and then the safety director tries different tactics, such as incentive programs or safety committees, to reduce the injury rate. The tactics may or may not be effective.

In a safety management system, the nine elements necessary for a system to succeed are clearly defined and understood by the management group. A gap analysis is performed, which reveals any deficiencies within the system. Priorities are chosen to close the gaps and responsibilities and accountabilities are spread throughout the management structure. The organization evaluates the effectiveness of the new efforts, building on successes and learning from failures.

The safety management system is an organized and structured means of ensuring that an organization is capable of achieving and maintaining high standards of safety performance. It is a comprehensive safety and health system that is proactive and preventive in nature.

The safety management system requires visible management leadership and commitment, involves employees in a meaningful way, uses both reactive measures and proactive measures and continuously improves.

According to the National Safety Council, the ultimate safety management system is comprised of:
- Administrative and management elements
- Operational and technical elements
- Cultural and behavioral elements

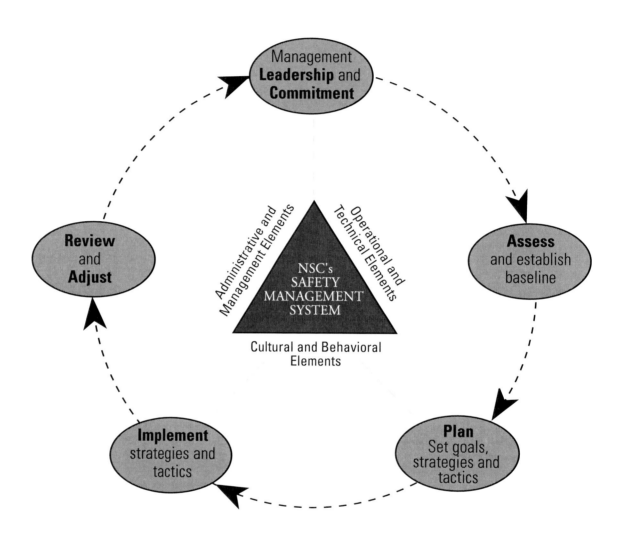

In general, the three sides of this safety management system "triangle" address the who, what, why and how of safety management. The "what" is the safety management system itself.

Administrative and management elements address the "why" of managing safety. This is answered through leadership and commitment, measuring safety performance, and communicating the results of managing safety.

Operational and technical elements of a system get to the "how" of safety management. Factors such as hazard control, workplace design, regulatory compliance, occupational health and environmental management are all addressed by operational and technical elements.

Cultural and behavioral elements address "who" is involved in such a system – all employees. Factors such as motivation, attitude, training and orientation are inherent these elements.

Within each of these sides of the triangle lie the following nine elements of a successful safety management system.

Element 1: Management leadership and commitment
Element 2: Organizational communications and system documentation
Element 3: Assessments, audits and continuous improvement
Element 4: Hazard recognition, evaluation and control
Element 5: Workplace design and engineering
Element 6: Operational safety and health programs
Element 7: Employee involvement
Element 8: Motivation, behavior and attitudes
Element 9: Training and orientation

element 1

management leadership
and commitment

Element 1: Management leadership and commitment

1.1 Management is ultimately responsible for leading the safety improvement process and for ensuring that all levels of line management implement the safety management system.

1.2 Management maintains a clearly stated safety and health policy and clearly communicates it to all employees.

1.3 Management creates clear safety program goals as well as corresponding objectives designed to meet those goals.

1.4 Management maintains a safety performance measurement and monitoring system that includes proactive performance measures for individuals at all levels of the organization.

1.5 Management shows visible participation and involvement on a regular basis in a variety of planned and proactive safety activities.

1.6 Management assigns responsibilities, roles and commensurate authority to managers and supervisors. They also provide assistance and training to support employee understanding of and capability to perform these roles.

1.7 Management allocates sufficient resources to support achievement of program goals and objectives.

1.8 Management uses a system of accountability to ensure managers, supervisors and employees accomplish their assigned safety responsibilities.

1.9 Management requires periodic reviews of programs, projects and activities to determine their effectiveness in achieving goals and objectives.

1.10 Management makes safety performance a key indicator of organizational excellence and integrates it into the business planning process.

Overview

If you were to ask business leaders about safety within their organizations, most would say safety is a top priority. As proof, these leaders might produce written safety policies, state that they frequently discuss safety at employee meetings, or point to the job safety analyses posted throughout their companies. Although these are important components of a safety effort, they must work in conjunction with a more important factor: the leadership's personal commitment to safety.

To build an effective safety culture, executive managers need a strong understanding of, and belief in, the benefits of safety, including reduced injuries, reduced costs associated with injury, improved public image, and increased morale, production, quality and, ultimately, profitability. When leaders understand these benefits, they naturally strive to integrate safety as a value in their business. They are willing to invest resources to improve the safety process, participate actively in safety efforts, and send a clear signal that safety is as important as productivity and profit.

It is only natural, then, that the first element in a successful safety management system is *management leadership and commitment*. When executive managers demonstrate a strong, genuine, continuous, and personal commitment to safety, their employees also will adopt safety as a value. Element 1 addresses the actions managers must take to establish and demonstrate their commitment to safety.

Management responsibility

In an effective safety management system, everyone shares responsibility for safety. Senior executives set the direction for safety; middle managers design practices and procedures needed to bring about desired results; and employees implement the safety practices. Everyone should be held accountable for performing assigned roles and responsibilities. If either the middle managers or employees fail to perform their safety duties, their performance appraisals must reflect this failure.

At the same time, top management must be *ultimately* responsible for safety. Executives should create and implement safety processes and procedures needed to minimize injuries and illness. Even if an employee violates a safety policy or procedure and subsequently gets injured, top management must recognize this as a failure within the safety management system.

Executives can show their commitment to a safety management system in a number of ways. Following are some suggestions.

- Put the safety management plan in writing and have the top management team sign it.
- Distribute this written plan to everyone in the business.
- Participate visibly in safety activities.
- Treat safety initiatives as though they are part of the job – not as though they are something else to do.

Element 1.1

Management is ultimately responsible for leading the safety improvement process and for ensuring that all levels of line management implement the safety management system.

- Request and read monthly status reports relating to safety. Examples include:
  - Injury reports
  - Job safety analysis and safety observation reports
  - Workers' compensation reports
  - Results of worksite analysis
- Create a budget for safety initiatives.
- Build safety into the business's strategic plan and operating goals.
- Build safety into the business's continuous improvement plan.
- Reward employees and supervisors for participating in safety activities.
  - Bonus to units who identify hazards and implement controls
  - Cash compensation for every safety suggestion implemented
  - A gift for publishing a story on OSHA's success story Web page *(http://www.osha.gov/SLTC/ergonomics/submit_successstory.html)*
- Assign safety management leadership to people who have a reputation for getting things done.
- Provide ongoing training to educate employees about safety.
- When the time comes to cut costs, leave the safety management plan intact.
- Insist that the purchasing department work with vendors who know and have agreed to abide by safety requirements.
- When the need for safety action arises, take the action immediately.
- Make performance in safety a key indicator of your business's performance.

Element 1.2

Management maintains a clearly stated safety and health policy and clearly communicates it to all employees.

Safety and health policy

Executive management should develop the safety and health policy with input from labor representatives and employees, and then distribute it throughout the organization. A well-written safety and health policy provides employees with overall guidance and direction relating to safety.

When developing a safety and health policy, executives should ensure the policy:

- Provides an overall sense of direction for safety
- Sets principles and guidelines for making safety decisions
- Provides a commitment to meaningful employee involvement in all aspects of the safety management process
- States top management's commitment to safety as a corporate value
- Reinforces top management's commitment to continuous improvement as a method for strengthening safety efforts
- Provides for periodic review to ensure it continues to meet the company's safety needs
- Has the signature of the most senior manager to demonstrate top management's commitment to safety

Business leaders should distribute the written safety and health policy to everyone in the organization and require managers and supervisors to meet with employees to discuss the policy. The policy needs to be included in new employee orientations and shared with vendors, customers and visitors so that everyone with a stake in the company understands the policy.

After an initial meeting, managers should consistently refer to the policy, reviewing it with all new employees. Leaders also should emphasize the safety and health policy at employee meetings and during performance reviews to help employees understand their role in upholding an effective safety and health policy.

In addition to the company-wide safety and health policy, each department should have its own set of procedures regarding basic safety and health work practices. The manager of the department, the employees, labor representatives and experienced safety professionals should jointly develop these safe work practices. It is especially important to include employees in this process as they are more likely to follow the practices and procedures they have had a role in developing.

Characteristics of effective
safe work practices and procedures

Effective safe work practices have several critical qualities. They are:

- **Clearly stated.** Use simple words stated in active voice without technical jargon. Examples of clearly stated safe work practices are "Wear hard hats onsite at all times" and "Report all injuries, no matter how slight."

- **Positively phrased.** People respond better to positive statements. Employees will be more likely to follow a positive statement, such as "Always wear rubber gloves on the job" than they would follow a negative statement of that same rule, "Don't forget to wear your rubber gloves."

- **Explained.** Employees are more likely to follow safe work practices they understand. For example, employees are more likely to follow good housekeeping practices once they understand the potential effects of disorder.

- **Fair.** Employees usually perceive necessary safe work practices as fair. Conversely, meaningless or excessively restrictive practices and selective enforcement can damage the credibility of *all* safe work practices.

Management should communicate safe work practices thoroughly, integrating them into departmental procedures, discussing them in departmental meetings and incorporating them into employee performance evaluations. Business leaders should consider making safe work practices more visible by publishing them in the company newsletter, on posters throughout the business and on pocket cards.

To make safety and health work practices effective, leaders must consistently enforce them. Employees should know the consequences of violating safe practices and procedures, and managers should apply these consequences evenly and fairly. When managers suddenly enforce a practice they have ignored in the past, the reprimanded employees may feel arbitrarily and unfairly singled out. Leaders should have a system for applying and documenting increasingly severe disciplinary actions for employees who violate safety procedures.

Having a safety and health policy and related departmental safe work practices sends a message to employees that the organization is serious about safety. Leaders should ensure these documents are well written, clearly communicated and consistently enforced. Employees should participate in the development of safe operating procedures, and then the safety staff should review the procedures for technical accuracy.

Element 1.3
Management creates clear safety program goals as well as corresponding objectives designed to meet those goals.

Goals and objectives

Safety planning is the process of determining what needs to be done to make the organization a safe place to work, who will do it, what resources are necessary and how long it will take. Business leaders conduct safety planning to determine the level of safety within an organization, resources necessary and time required to improve that level, and identify the staff to implement the improvement process. There are multiple planning levels, each with a safety component.

Vision

A vision is an ideal picture of the future, and often uses visual words and phrases. A vision statement does not clarify procedures or include much detail. Rather, its main purpose is to inspire and motivate employees by giving them a picture of the possible future. A safety vision would most likely describe a lofty goal to have an incident-free workplace.

Mission

An organization's mission statement describes what it does and why it is in business. It defines the organization's products, services, industry segments, customers and geographical markets. If leaders are serious about making safety a value, they will address safety in the mission statement. After all, there is no stronger way to send a message about safety than to include it in the document that defines the organization.

Sample mission statement

To provide leadership, commitment, expectations, coordination and services in driving the Safety and Health Process, thereby adding value by reducing injuries and illnesses and associated costs. This, in turn, benefits our facilities, business units, Company and our Most Valuable Asset, "OUR PEOPLE."

Strategies

Strategies are statements describing how leaders in the organization will accomplish the mission. Executives write them at the organizational level and address a period of 3 to 5 years into the future. Safety strategies specifically identify how executives will accomplish the safety component of the mission. Here are some examples of safety strategies:

- Implement a safety management system by [date].
- Reduce to zero insurance increases due to preventable causes in the next fiscal year.
- Decrease overall safety and health-related fines by 50 percent in the next fiscal year.

Goals

Goals describe what managers will do at the departmental level. Goals are specific and measurable statements conveying the actions a department will take to carry out organizational strategies. Following are some goals managers might use to support organizational strategy:

- Create a safety and health policy statement by [date].
- Attain a level of 100 percent reporting of incidents.
- Decrease the department rate of incidents by 60 percent for the next fiscal year.

Objectives

Objectives describe what steps individual employees will take to carry out departmental goals. Following are some examples of individual objectives:

- Facilitate [number] meetings to communicate the safety and health policy to employees.
- Provide training to every employee on the importance of and procedures for reporting incidents.
- Inspect containers for compliance with the labeling requirements of the Hazard Communication Standard and correct those out of compliance.

When an organization plans effectively, it can use its goals and objectives to measure safety performance. Each goal and objective becomes a target or benchmark against which to measure progress. At the end of the planning period, leaders can assess which goals and objectives they achieved and, based on this assessment, determine how far the organization has come in achieving its safety strategies.

Performance measurement

Measurement is the process of assessing an organization's efforts, then tracking progress through time. Safety measurements allow leaders to assess how well their safety efforts are working. Executives who are committed to safety will require safety measurements as a part of everyone's job.

Element 1.4

Management maintains a safety performance measurement and monitoring system that includes proactive performance measures for individuals at all levels of the organization.

Good safety measurements have four important characteristics. First, they align with the organization's safety strategies, goals and objectives. The best way to know if a strategy or goal is working is to measure it and see improvement.

Characteristics of good measurements

- They align with the organization's safety strategies, goals and objectives.
- They encourage safe behavior and discourage at-risk behavior.
- They improve the safety management system.
- They are used by people at all levels of the organization.

Safety measurements also encourage safe behaviors and discourage at-risk behaviors. For example, most organizations measure the number of incidents occurring on the job – and this is desirable; however, if leaders place too much emphasis on that single measurement, they might cause an underreporting of incidents. To counteract this effect, leaders should include activity and process-oriented measurements, such as tracking the number of safety observations.

Executives use safety measurements to improve the safety management system. The first time they take a measurement, it serves as a baseline against which they may compare all future measurements. As leaders see their measurements improve, they will know their safety efforts are working. Finally, executives should require people at all levels of the organization to take safety measurements.

Clearly, there is no shortage of safety measurements. The challenge for executives is to select the measurements that will provide the best information about safety in the organization. A good approach is to start small by selecting just a few measurements and doing them well. Once leaders see improvements in the measurements they have selected, they can add a few more measurements. In this way, they continuously improve their safety measurement system even as the measurements themselves are helping them improve safety.

Element 1.5

Management shows visible participation and involvement on a regular basis in a variety of planned and proactive safety activities.

Management involvement

When employees see senior leaders participating in safety and health efforts, they are more likely to practice safety and health in their own jobs. Executives can be involved in safety and health in many ways. Following are some of the most important.

- Follow all safety and health procedures and rules.
- Address safety and health issues in the business plan, and give them equal status with other business issues, such as productivity and cost containment.
- Make sure safety and health efforts have proper funding.
- Pay attention to and ask questions about safety and health measurements.
- Hold managers accountable for the safety and health results by making safety performance a part of performance reviews.

- Attend safety meetings and training to show visibility and demonstrate support.
- Conduct a safety meeting or facilitate a safety training program.
- Require proactive measurements, such as safety observations, and ask questions about the results.

Executives should actively plan their involvement by selecting activities that visibly show their support for safety, scheduling these activities on their calendars and following through with them. When people in the organization see their top managers participating in safety, they too will take an interest in making their own jobs safe.

Responsibilities and roles

Every employee in an organization should be responsible for safety. Even if there is a safety and health department, its role should be to coach, guide and help others in the organization carry out their safety responsibilities.

One of top management's key responsibilities is making sure employees' safety roles are formal, assigned and understood. Once executives identify the safety roles in the organization, they should include them in every job description. Following are some typical safety roles in an organization.

Safety and health staff
- Follow all safety and health procedures and rules.
- Assist and guide top management in supporting important safety and health initiatives.
- Advise management and employees on the formulation of safety and health policy.
- Act as a catalyst for initiating and implementing important safety and health initiatives.
- Provide expertise, advice, information and tools relating to effective safety and health management.
- Focus on developing systems for prevention, rather than on responding to every incident one-by-one.
- Work to engage all employees in the safety and health effort.
- Make resources available for continued development of safety and health issues.

Managers
- Follow all safety and health procedures and rules.
- Instill good safety and health behavior in supervisors and employees.
- Reward honest analysis rather than covering up problems for fear of retribution.
- Reward systemic policies or procedures that prevent cover-ups of safety problems or incidents.
- Request safe production, not production and safety.
- Reward supervisors who properly train and coach their employees.
- Consider safety and health when planning for facilities or equipment.

Element 1.6

Management assigns responsibilities, roles and commensurate authority to managers and supervisors. They also provide assistance and training to support employee understanding of, and capability to perform, these roles.

13

- Participate in finding solutions for safety and health problems.
- Reward supervisors for correcting safety and health problems.

Supervisors

- Follow all safety and health procedures and rules.
- Hold workplace safety meetings that produce measurable results.
- Actively develop and implement safety and health programs.
- Praise and reward employees who identify potential hazards.
- Encourage employees to be involved in safety and health efforts.
- Consult with the safety department before there is a problem.
- Monitor implementation and follow through of safety and health efforts.
- Get involved in teaching some of the safety and health training programs.
- Participate as a communications link with employees on safety.

Employees

- Follow all safety and health procedures and rules.
- Participate in conducting safety and health investigations.
- Participate in finding solutions to safety and health problems.
- Alert the appropriate people about any safety or health hazard.
- Get involved in showing new employees the safety procedures.

Once top management has assigned safety roles and responsibilities, it must then provide coaching and training so employees know how to perform their assigned duties. Coaching should be ongoing. Managers should frequently discuss safety issues, ideas and concerns with employees. Training should be conducted at least annually; should provide a review of employees' safety responsibilities; and should introduce and explain new safety initiatives.

When employees understand their safety roles and responsibilities, they will work hard to make the organization safe.

Element 1.7
Management allocates sufficient resources to support achievement of program goals and objectives.

Sufficient resources

It is difficult for employees to carry out their safety responsibilities if they lack sufficient resources. Top management must ensure employees have adequate time, staff, space, equipment and money to achieve their safety goals and responsibilities. Some specific resources required for implementing a safety management system are:

- Time to create safety strategies, goals and action plans.
- Time and budgetary resources to carry out the strategies, goals and action plans.
- Time to communicate adequately about safety.
- Money in the budget to pay for audits, assessments and other safety initiatives.
- Time to conduct hazard evaluation.
- Money to make improvements identified in hazard evaluation.
- Money to design and engineer a safe workplace.

- Time and money to implement safety programs and initiatives.
- Time to work with employees to get them involved.
- Time and money to train employees in safety and health.
- Time to ensure the right people are hired for the job.

A system of accountability

As important as it is to assign safety roles and responsibilities to employees, what happens if they fail to fulfill their responsibilities? How do leaders hold their employees accountable for their safety duties? The most effective system of accountability is the performance evaluation. If employees know their supervisors will evaluate them on their safety objectives, they are likely to work harder to achieve them. Additionally, top managers should have at least a portion of their bonuses contingent on attaining their safety strategies so they, too will focus on these responsibilities.

Another effective method for getting accountability is to charge back incident costs or increased insurance premiums to the department where the incident occurred. Nothing gets managers' attention faster than knowing an incident will affect their bottom line.

Element 1.8

Management uses a system of accountability to ensure managers, supervisors and employees accomplish their assigned safety responsibilities.

Methods for achieving accountability

- The performance appraisal
- Charge-back of the costs of incidents
- Communication of safety information throughout the organization
- Sponsorship of activities focusing on achieving safety goals
- Consistent top management interest in safety measurements

A third way to get accountability is to communicate safety information throughout the organization. Executives can do this by posting the results on company bulletin boards, publishing them in newsletters or discussing them in monthly meetings. When safety results are available for all to see, both managers and employees are likely to work harder to make the results positive. There is a word of caution regarding this method. Leaders should take care to convey the information positively and proactively. The idea is to talk about safety results as a method for improving safety, not as a method for punishment. If employees or leaders fear punishment or retribution, they may hide incidents and cover up other safety problems.

Another way to get accountability is to sponsor activities focusing on achieving safety goals. For example, if a department sponsors a hazard hunt and offers prizes to the people who identify the most (or most dangerous) hazards, employees are more likely to focus on their hazard communication objectives. Other activities that can promote accountability are safety fairs and safety training sessions.

The final method for getting accountability is simply to have top management take consistent interest in safety measurements. If managers know their vice presidents will be reviewing and asking about their safety initiatives, they will be more likely to focus on achieving them.

Element 1.9

Management requires periodic
reviews of programs,
projects and activities to
determine their effectiveness
in achieving goals and objectives.

Periodic reviews

How will leaders know if their organization's safety initiatives are succeeding? Most likely, they will see – or hear about – results indicating a safety improvement (or decline). As interesting as this anecdotal evidence might be, it is an unreliable way to measure safety effectiveness. Instead, an organization needs a formal, systematic approach to reviewing its safety initiatives.

Safety review does not have to be complicated or difficult. The first thing leaders should do is tap into review systems that already exist. For example, most organizations already have a performance review process and, if they are serious about safety, they already have safety goals integrated into this process. So when it is time to sit down and discuss performance, leaders should simply make certain they also discuss each individual's safety performance.

Another resource leaders can use is the review of the organization's strategic plan. Once again, organizations with a safety management system will already have safety priorities built into their strategic plans. When it is time to review these plans, leaders can easily review the safety priorities that were a part of the plan.

Other sources for review are safety audits, job safety analysis and safety observation. Each of these programs has a built in analysis enabling organizations to review their safety efforts. In addition, leaders can review their safety management system by completing the assessments at the end of each chapter in this book.

When reviewing safety efforts, executives should examine both the strengths and the areas for improvement. They should document the strengths and share them with others in the organization so they can make the same improvements. They should make the areas for improvement a part of the next year's goals and objectives.

When leaders consistently review their organization's safety efforts, then make improvements based on the review, they are practicing continuous improvement. Through time, these safety reviews will show a dramatic improvement in safety results.

Element 1.10

Management makes
safety performance a key
indicator of organizational
excellence and integrates it into the
business planning process.

A key indicator of excellence

There is a lot of work involved with leading the implementation of a safety management system. In the end, though, safety will turn out to be a good business decision. Ultimately, outstanding safety performance creates organizational excellence.

When leaders integrate safety initiatives into the business plan and give them the same weight as production, cost control, quality control and marketing, they find their organizations achieve excellent performance. Research is emerging that shows a focus on safety not only decreases the costs associated with injuries/illnesses and lost workdays, it also increases productivity. For example, in the Paducah, KY plant of USEC Inc., it has been found that "…a safety-based culture has enabled it to operate efficiently and reach all-time production records. The plant has maintained 100 percent delivery of its product on schedule and has constantly met quality standards. Factory costs have been reduced by 20 percent during the last 5 years and a 24 percent improvement in employee productivity has been achieved based on the unit output per employee." [From National Safety Council, Case Studies in Safety & Productivity, 2000, p. 18.]

Element 1: Management leadership and commitment review

Issues/questions	In place			Action plan
	Yes	No	Partially	(if "no" or "partially")
1. Does management set a positive example by following the organization's safety and health procedures?				
2. Does the organization have a safety and health policy?				
3. Does this policy address: • Management's commitment to safety and health? • How safety stacks up as a priority against production and cost-effectiveness? • What the organization expects from each employee relative to safety and health? • What the organization expects from its safety and health function? • Identification of who makes decisions about safety and health? • Identification of who has authority to implement safety and health policy? • A summary of how the organization handles safety and health issues? • The degree of risk the organization is willing to accept.				
4. Is the safety and health policy distributed and communicated throughout the organization?				
5. Does the organization have the following planning components in place: • A safety and health vision? • A safety and health mission statement? • Safety and health strategies? • Departmental safety and health goals? • Individual safety and health objectives?				
6. Are safety and health work practices and procedures in place? Are they clear, positive and fair?				

Element 1: Management leadership and commitment review

Issues/questions	In place			Action plan
	Yes	No	Partially	(if "no" or "partially")
7. Do safety and health work practices and procedures reflect input by all employees?				
8. Are all managers and employees assigned safety roles and responsibilities?				
9. Are these roles and responsibilities identified in the job description?				
10. Does senior management participate in safety and health efforts?				
11. Have measures been developed to monitor compliance with performance standards?				
12. Is compliance with performance standards monitored and reviewed on a regular basis? Is the frequency adequate?				
13. Do employees receive annual training regarding safety and health issues?				
14. Is an effective safety and health orientation program in place for new employees?				
15. Is a mechanism in place for performance accountability?				
16. Have performance standards been developed for all tasks?				
17. Does management review performance reports and provide feedback?				

element 2

organization communications
and system documentation

Element 2: Organization communications and system documentation

2.1 Management establishes and maintains policies for communicating information about the safety management system. They include methods for conveying, documenting and responding to both internal and external communications.

2.2 Management has a mechanism for communicating safety and health information from the top leadership, through all levels of management and supervision, to employees.

2.3 Management maintains a mechanism for getting feedback from employees to the appropriate level of management, including senior management.

2.4 Management maintains a record-keeping system that includes a clearly written document control procedure. This system identifies:
  2.4.1 Who has access to and responsibility for maintaining the record-keeping and document control system
  2.4.2 What documents, records or other pertinent data the system should maintain (documents should be retrievable, readily identifiable, legible and dated)
  2.4.3 How long the system will maintain the records and how the system will keep documents up-to-date
  2.4.4 Where records are located and how people can access them

2.5 The record-keeping documents generate information enabling the organization to evaluate safety performance and make improvements. This information includes the following.
  2.5.1 Injury and illness data, including off-the-job injury data and related costs
  2.5.2 Data from incident investigations
  2.5.3 Industrial hygiene surveys and exposure monitoring results
  2.5.4 Results of (as well as status of corrective action from) safety performance reviews, management assessments, third party audits and inspections
  2.5.5 Safety policy, procedures, safety work practices, program objectives and goal status
  2.5.6 Roles and responsibilities for program areas
  2.5.7 Process safety reviews, risk assessments and hazard analysis
  2.5.8 Elements of the safety management system and their connection to each other

Overview

Executives should use two key methods to keep employees informed about and involved in safety. The first is open, two-way communication. Two-way communication allows executives to keep employees up-to-date with safety policies, procedures, roles, responsibilities, goals and results. It also encourages employees to tell leaders about problems and issues with safety. By making it easy for communication to flow both ways, leaders can quickly assess and continuously improve safety in their organizations.

The second method for keeping employees informed about safety is to keep accurate records. A good record-keeping system allows executives to document safety policies and procedures, and provides them with reliable information for analysis, decision making and measuring continuous improvement.

Element 2 describes how to establish and maintain a communication policy and offers mechanisms for disseminating information to and receiving information from employees. In addition, this element describes how to maintain a record-keeping system that includes a clearly defined document control procedure and generates information enabling executives to evaluate performance and make improvements.

Communication policy

Element 1 addressed the importance of having a clearly stated safety and health policy; however, this element will have limited usefulness if executives fail to communicate the safety and health policy throughout the organization. In fact, no safety initiative can be effective unless all managers and employees know about it and understand it.

For this reason, executives should establish and maintain a communication policy covering every safety program or initiative. This includes:

- Organizational safety procedures
- Job safety procedures
- Lockout/tagout procedures
- Confined space procedures
- Material Safety Data Sheet procedures
- Incident investigation
- Safety inspections
- Job safety analysis
- Job safety observation

Executives should communicate this information to everyone within the organization. To do this, they must address such questions as:

- How will employees learn about the safety program or initiative?
- How will employees learn about changes and updates to existing programs or initiatives?
- Who is responsible for communicating the policy or initiative to each level of the organization?

Element 2.1

Management establishes and maintains policies for communicating information about the safety management system. These policies include methods for conveying, documenting and responding to both internal and external communications.

- Should executives require employees to sign documents verifying they were informed of the policy or initiative?
- Will executives require supervisors and employees to document that they are following the safety policy/initiative?
- How will supervisors and employees disseminate the data they generate from this policy/initiative?
- Who will answer questions (either internal or external) relating to the policy/initiative?

To communicate safety policy, executives can create one general communication policy and apply it to every safety program or initiative. This approach requires only one policy to cover every program/initiative. The disadvantage of this type of singular communication policy is that a "one size fits all" approach may not be effective for addressing every safety initiative in the organization.

Conversely, executives may choose to create a specific communication policy for each new safety program or initiative. The benefit of this approach is that it can address the specific communication requirements of each particular program. The drawback, of course, is that executives must write a communication policy for each new safety program or initiative.

Some executives may choose to use a combination of these two approaches by writing an overall communication policy applying to all safety programs and initiatives, and then adding specific guidelines applying to each individual initiative.

Sample safety and health communication policy

Safety and health is of the utmost importance. In the interest of safety, we will constantly evaluate our safety efforts and initiate changes and improvements. The following policy will ensure all managers and employees receive information regarding our safety initiatives:

- Departments will present any new or changed safety programs or initiatives to the leadership team.
- Members of the leadership team will present the initiative to their direct reports, and then require their managers and supervisors to present it to employees.
- Executives and managers will encourage employees to ask questions regarding the initiative. Managers will send these questions to the department that created the change.
- The department will assemble a FAQ sheet addressing employee questions.
- The department will work with company trainers and supervisors to ensure training on the new initiative is included in employee orientation and other training programs.
- If the initiative is a legal requirement, managers must require employees to sign a statement verifying they received the training/information.
- The department will answer ongoing questions regarding the initiative.

Leadership communication

Executives should use the safety communication policy to disseminate information about safety and health throughout the organization. Top management must ensure their direct reports pass safety information to their department managers and supervisors. In turn, managers and supervisors must give the appropriate information to employees.

The communication policy should not be the *only* means of communicating about safety; executives should use the policy in *conjunction with* other methods for getting the safety message out. Some examples of these techniques include:

- Mention safety policy in the company's annual report.
- Discuss safety in customer communications, such as brochures and catalogs.
- Discuss safety at annual employee meetings.
- Schedule brown-bag lunches where safety is the topic.
- Provide safety videos in the break room.
- Post safety messages on company bulletin boards or in company newsletters.
- Distribute safety messages on computer screen savers.
- Add safety messages to company letterhead.
- Display safety messages in the company lobby and break rooms.
- Offer a visual display of safety data throughout the company.

When deciding which communication techniques to use, executives should consider a combination of written, verbal and non-verbal communication.

Written communication

Written communication is visual, permanent and can be either formal, as in the case of procedures documentation, or informal, as in the case of short messages appearing on a computer screen saver. Executives should consider using written communication when conveying complicated, technical or legal information. They can require employees to sign a document acknowledging receipt and understanding of the information. Written materials also enable employees to refer to the distributed information later.

A disadvantage of written communication is that it is one-way and executives have no way of knowing if employees understood the message. To overcome this disadvantage, executives need to follow up communications to determine if employees have any questions or need clarification.

Some communications must be written. Examples include safety policies and procedures, incident investigation reports, job safety analysis reports, work order requests, and statistical summaries of injuries and illness.

Verbal communication

Verbal communication is face-to-face, in-the-moment, and can be either formal, as in the case of a company presentation, or informal, as in the case of thanking an employee for a job well done. Verbal communication allows leaders to see employee responses and to ask questions to confirm understanding of the message.

Element 2.2

Management has a mechanism for communicating safety and health information from the top leadership, through all levels of management and supervision, to employees.

Executives should use verbal communication when they want to convey information quickly and informally. For example, a supervisor might discuss job procedures with an employee and demonstrate the safe way to perform a task. A supervisor also might use verbal communication to compliment an employee for performing a job safely. Executives should require verbal coaching as a part of formal initiatives such as safety inspections, job safety analysis, safety training and job safety observations.

A disadvantage of verbal communication is that it can be misunderstood. To overcome this disadvantage, leaders should ask questions to ensure recipients understood the message as intended. For important communication, such as the verbal coaching required with formal safety initiatives, supervisors should summarize the discussion in writing and give a copy to the appropriate employees.

Combining written and verbal communication

To achieve the best safety results, executives should use both written and verbal communication. If their primary method of communicating is a written document such as a job safety analysis or safety inspection, they should, nonetheless, also provide verbal follow up to allow employees to ask questions and to ensure their understanding. If verbal communication, such as giving feedback to employees, is their primary method for communicating, they also should write a summary of the discussion to have permanent documentation.

Improving written and verbal communication

Executives can improve both their written and verbal communication by practicing the following suggestions:

- Plan the message. Decide what the objective of the communication is; then ask how best to accomplish it.
- Consider the receiver. Ask the following questions about the recipient:
  - What type of communication does he/she respond to best?
  - When and where will the recipient be able to receive the message without distractions?
  - Does the receiver have any biases or strong feelings about the message?
  - Does the receiver have any disabilities, such as illiteracy, hearing loss or impaired vision?
  - How can the leader help the recipient keep an open mind regarding the message?
- Be brief and specific.
- Avoid jargon.
- Adjust for potential biases, cultural differences, etc.

Non-verbal communication

Executives must consider non-verbal communication when forming safety policies and practices. In fact, the strongest safety messages come from what executives do –

not from what they say. Top management must teach their leadership team how to make their non-verbal communication consistent with safety policies and procedures.

To begin, top management must require every manager and supervisor in the organization to follow all the safety rules and procedures. For example, leaders who expect employees to wear protective headwear or safety glasses should wear the appropriate gear themselves.

In most instances, when a leader's actions (non-verbal communication) conflict with a written safety policy, employees will follow their leader's example, not the policy. Executives should take advantage of their employees' tendency to follow their lead by modeling the *positive* safety behaviors they want.

Similarly, executives need to consider non-verbal messages sent by business decisions. For example, a critical piece of equipment that becomes a safety hazard should not be used merely to continue production and meet financial goals. Doing so would send the non-verbal message to employees that production is more important than safety.

To prevent this mistake, executives must direct managers and supervisors to solve production problems while keeping the workplace safe. Supervisors need to know they can take the unsafe equipment off-line, without punishment, until the safety problem is fixed. Executives must teach the leadership team that a safe workplace also is a profitable workplace. Conversely, an unsafe workplace can hurt profitability. When the leadership team believes this, their non-verbal behavior will reflect the organization's written policies and procedures.

Employee feedback

To be effective, communication about safety must flow in all directions. While it is important to get information to employees, it is even more critical to hear back from them. Employees who are on the front line doing the job know where the safety problems are, and they probably also know good ways to fix them. An effective safety management system contains mechanisms for capturing this information from employees.

One of the best ways to obtain information from employees is to build a culture of open communication in which employees are encouraged to share ideas. Initially, employees may be reluctant to speak up for fear of reprimand; however, if executives create a system that supports and rewards employee suggestions, employees will eventually learn to offer their ideas freely. Methods leaders can use to encourage employee input include:

- Scheduling regular question and answer sessions with employees. Usually, the departmental supervisor should conduct these meetings; however, senior management also should occasionally spend time talking with employees about safety.
- Requiring tailgate meetings before major projects so employees can talk about potential safety issues during the project and learn ideas for handling them.
- Including a section in the company newsletter in which employees can ask questions about safety and have them answered.

Element 2.3

Management maintains a mechanism for getting feedback from employees to the appropriate level of management, including senior management.

- Creating and maintaining a suggestion box, then encouraging employees to use it if they want to voice safety concerns anonymously.
- Conducting periodic written safety surveys to probe attitudes about, and knowledge of, safety.
- Creating and maintaining safety initiatives that include an employee feedback component. Examples of such initiatives are safety observation tours, job safety analysis and safety inspections.

For any of the above mechanisms to work, employees must feel confident that they can speak up without fear of retaliation and that management will take their ideas seriously. Executives need to teach managers and supervisors to respond to employee suggestions in a positive way. This includes having supervisors implement as many employee ideas a possible. In addition, executives must provide an avenue for employees to go directly to senior management if they feel their supervisors are unresponsive to their concerns. For example, they could create and maintain a toll-free hotline that employees can call to voice their concerns anonymously.

When top leaders listen to and act upon employee safety concerns, they strengthen the safety management system by making employees an integral part of the process.

Element 2.4

Management maintains a record-keeping system including a clearly written document control procedure.

Record-keeping systems

Record keeping is an important component of an effective safety management system. Good records allow executives to document safety policies and procedures, providing them with reliable information for analysis, decision making and continuous improvement.

However, top managers often fail to require good records for a variety of reasons. In some instances, they feel it is simply too difficult or time consuming to collect and store detailed safety information. In other instances, they worry that safety records could incriminate them in the event of a lawsuit. These concerns are minor in comparison to the benefits of having an effective record-keeping system. In their article entitled "Legal Aspects of Safety and Health Reports and Records," Patrick R. Tyson and David L. Smith identify the following benefits of effective record keeping.[1]

- Supervisors and managers are more likely to address hazards if they see them in writing.
- Records from safety inspections, safety audits, incident investigations and job safety observations provide visible checklists of things leaders need to address for a safer workplace.
- OSHA reduces its penalties by 15 to 25 percent when an employer can produce written records demonstrating a good-faith effort to address safety issues.
- If an employee sues an employer due to a safety incident, the courts are more likely to rule in favor of the employer if it has written records showing it has consistently identified and addressed safety issues.

Footnote: [1]Patrick R. Tyson, David L. Smith, "Legal aspects of safety and health reports and records," Construction Newsletter, March/April, 1999, pp. 3-4.

Document control procedure

For the best possible record-keeping system, management needs to create and maintain a document control procedure. This procedure should specify everything employees need to know about preparing, accessing and using the company's safety and health system. A good document control procedure identifies the following information:

- Who has access to and responsibility for maintaining the record-keeping and document control system?

  Element 2.4.1

- What documents, records or other pertinent data the system should maintain (documents should be retrievable, readily identifiable, legible and dated)?

  Element 2.4.2

- How long the system will maintain the records and how the system will keep documents up-to-date?

  Element 2.4.3

- Where records are located and how people can access them?

  Element 2.4.4

Sample safety and health documentation

Background:	This section provides a brief summary of why the program or initiative is important and why it is a part of the company's safety management system.
Required documents:	This section lists the documents required for the safety and health program/initiative. It should list appropriate: • Policy statements • Instructions, guidelines or procedures • Applicable training materials • Checklists • Forms • Other documents pertinent to the program/initiative
Policy:	This section states the policy itself.
Scope and responsibility:	This section describes to whom the program or initiative applies.
Procedures:	This section should provide detailed, step-by-step instructions for implementing the safety program or initiative. In addition, it identifies those responsible for carrying out each step.
Additional information:	This section lists any documents relating to or providing additional information about the safety program or initiative.
Revision summary:	This section provides a summary of all revisions including: • The revision number • The date of the revision • A brief summary of the revision

In addition to the above information, a good document control system contains detailed summaries of every safety and health program or initiative in the company. Each person responsible for a safety program or initiative should write the summary and provide the following:
- Background information
- List of required documents such as forms or procedures
- The relevant policy statement
- Procedures for implementation
- Any additional pertinent information
- Revision summary

Element 2.5
The record-keeping documents generate information enabling the organization to evaluate performance and make improvements.

Element 2.5.1
Element 2.5.2
Element 2.5.3
Element 2.5.4

Element 2.5.5
Element 2.5.6
Element 2.5.7
Element 2.5.8

Record-keeping information

A good record-keeping system provides information that helps executives evaluate safety performance and make improvements. A good record-keeping system also provides accurate and complete records about who within the company is adhering to standards and regulations.

A good record-keeping system should include:
- Injury and illness data, including off-the-job injury data and related costs
- Data from incident investigations
- Industrial hygiene surveys and exposure monitoring results
- Results of (as well as status of corrective action from) safety performance reviews, management assessments, third party audits and inspections
- Safety policy, procedures, safety work practices, program objectives and goal status
- Roles and responsibilities for program areas
- Process safety reviews, risk assessments and hazard analysis
- Elements of the safety management system and their connection to each other

Data analysis

It is not enough for executives simply to collect safety and health information – they also need to study it to identify problem areas and to learn about trends that may need attention. Following are examples of problems executives might identify by analyzing safety data:
- A high incidence of injuries associated with a particular piece of equipment or a certain procedure
- A discovery of near miss incidents in a specific department that reveals a hazard that could eventually cause a serious injury
- An incident rate that appears related to the level of an employee's experience (could indicate complacency or sloppiness, a need for refresher training, or unresolved problems with equipment or processes)
- An incident and illness rate that appears related to the shift and the time of day (could indicate problems with fatigue or inadequate supervision on later shifts)

- An incident and illness rate that appears related to specific equipment and tools (could indicate that specific processes, equipment or tools may need updating or changing)

Cost analysis

Once executives have analyzed the safety and health data, they will undoubtedly decide to make some changes and improvements. Managers and supervisors also may recommend changes. The executives who allocate budgets will find these changes much easier to approve if they see a clear cost benefit to them.

Managers can demonstrate the cost-effectiveness of their proposals by calculating the expenses relating to having an incident at their facility, then showing that the proposed initiative will reduce the occurrence of incidents. To calculate the cost of an incident, managers and supervisors can consider the following factors.

- Workers compensation costs
- Wages of employees who are nonproductive during their involvement with the incident
- Wages of injured parties in excess of workers' compensation payments
- Uninsured medical costs paid by the company
- Overtime needed to make up for lost production time or repairs
- Decreased output of recovering (but working) injured employees
- Hiring and training costs for replacement employees
- Lower productivity for temporary or replacement employees
- Time chargeable to the incident spent on claims, record keeping, investigation and reporting
- Lost production
- Repair or scrap of damaged product
- Equipment and materials repair and replacement costs

When top executives see that proactive safety measures have a positive financial effect, they are more willing to approve expenditures.

Element 2: Organizational communications and system documentation review

Issues/questions	In place			Action plan (if "no" or "partially")
	Yes	No	Partially	
1. Has management established a formal policy for communicating safety and health information throughout the organization?				
2. Does management routinely communicate on safety subjects?				
3. Does management have informal communications with employees to present safety tips, update them on progress toward safety goals or ask them to take action?				
4. Does management require minutes at each safety meeting?				
5. Does management report the results of safety and health programs/initiatives to everyone in the company?				
6. Does management use safety visuals, such as posters, to promote general safety awareness and remind employees of key safety issues?				
7. Does management provide safety and health publications, such as booklets, to employees, so they can read them at their own pace? Are multilingual versions available?				
8. Does management use training and education programs to communicate information required by law, such as contained in Material Safety Data Sheets or materials for "hazmat" or "hazcom" employees?				
9. Has management established a document control procedure?				
10. Does that procedure identify the following? • Who has access to and responsibility for maintaining the system? • What documents, records or other pertinent data the system should maintain? • How long the system will maintain the records and how the system will keep documents up-to-date? • Where records are located and how people can access them?				

Element 2: Organizational communications and system documentation review

Issues/questions	In place			Action plan (if "no" or "partially")
	Yes	No	Partially	
11. Does management require data collection and analysis?				
12. Does management require, read and provide feedback on periodic occupational injury and illness reports and other related reports?				
13. Does management allocate resources for data collection and analysis activities?				
14. Does management compare data to similar companies or between similar departments within the same company?				
15. Does management understand the financial impact of safety?				
16. Does management require off-the-job data and support an off-the-job program?				
17. Does management post an annual OSHA log summary and leave it up for a minimum of one month?				
18. Does the safety and health department have access to a computer?				
19. Is computer hardware adequate to maintain records?				
20. Has management purchased software to be used for tracking and analysis of safety and health data?				
21. Does management maintain procedures for complete, timely, accurate and uniform data collection?				
22. Does management require the routine updating of records?				
23. Does management maintain data on workplace conditions?				
24. Does management maintain inspection reports for easy follow up and analysis?				

element 3

assessments, audits and continuous improvement

Element 3: Assessments, audits and continuous improvement

3.1 Management periodically conducts safety management system assessments to learn the effectiveness of the current system, identify and prioritize areas of improvement and propose changes to enhance the safety management system. They ensure the results are documented and entered into the occupational safety and health record-keeping system.

3.2 Management establishes formal policy and procedures for periodic audits. The business plan and the organization's safety and health priorities drive the design for the audit system, which is preventive in nature and focuses on the audits most likely to expose hazards and unsafe conditions. Employees at all levels of the organization participate and give input into the development of the audit system. The final system includes the following components:

    3.2.1 A summary of the types of audits to be conducted

    3.2.2 The scope and purpose of each audit

    3.2.3 Defined roles, responsibilities, qualifications and competencies of team members

    3.2.4 A schedule for the various types of audits

    3.2.5 Standards and procedures for conducting the audits

    3.2.6 Observations, findings and management response

    3.2.7 A program review of one or all of the elements of the safety management system

3.3 The safety management system is based on the principles of continuous improvement, which include the following:

    3.3.1 Management commitment to, and leadership of, the continuous improvement process

    3.3.2 Assessing the current situation and identifying the issues using the nine elements as a guide

    3.3.3 Planning measurable improvement goals, strategies and tactics

    3.3.4 Implementing the plans

    3.3.5 Reviewing and adjusting the process to facilitate constant improvement

Overview

When executives create safety processes and procedures at their organizations, they need to know managers and employees will implement them, and they will be successful. To learn if employees are following safe practices and procedures, leaders should conduct safety audits. Then, to learn how effective these practices and procedures are, leaders should assess them.

Element 3 provides the knowledge and methods required to develop a safety assessment and audit system. It introduces the types of assessments and audits leaders can use, provides guidelines for creating and implementing assessment and auditing programs, and introduces the continuous improvement process. Continuous improvement enables executives to identify gaps in the safety system, then select and implement priorities for improvement.

Periodic assessments

An assessment is a comprehensive review of an organization's safety management system. The best assessment is one that reviews all nine elements in the safety management system and provides executives with answers to the following questions:

- Are procedures in place for each safety and health program and initiative in the organization?
- Has management identified the people responsible for implementing safety and health policies, processes and procedures?
- Has management provided proper training for these people so they can do their jobs?
- Is there a system for following up to ensure everyone is fulfilling his or her safety and health responsibilities?
- Is there an adequate system for keeping safety and health records?
- Is there an adequate system for using data from the records to make safety and health improvements?

Upon completion of an assessment, executives should have a clear understanding of the major organizational trends and operational deficiencies relating to safety and health. In addition, they should identify 5 to 10 key strategies for improving safety and health in the organization.

Frequency of assessment

Because conducting a comprehensive safety and health assessment requires considerable time, executives should consider doing it every 2 to 3 years. The first assessment performed establishes a baseline of measurements that reveal the current performance of the safety system. The baseline of measurements also should be used to prepare strategies for improving safety and health. With each subsequent comprehensive assessment, results should be compared with the baseline results. Of course, each new set of results then becomes the baseline for future assessments, and executive should use the latest results to create new strategies.

Element 3.1

Management periodically conducts safety management system assessments to learn the effectiveness of the current system, identify and prioritize areas of improvement and propose changes to enhance the safety management system. They ensure the results are documented and entered into the occupational safety and health record-keeping system.

In small organizations – particularly those in service industries – executives may be able to identify program deficiencies through frequent, but less formal, inspections; however, management should still periodically assess the acceptance and effectiveness of its safety and health policies.

Assessment process

The assessment process itself consists of three key steps. First, the assessor performs a thorough review of the organization's safety and health documents including policies and procedures, summary reports from the various safety and health programs and any written plans.

Next, the assessor conducts interviews with managers, supervisors and employees. In these interviews, the assessor learns whether employees are following the written policies and procedures and if there are any key safety or health concerns. If employees are not following procedures, the assessor should find out why.

In the final step, the assessor goes to the various worksites and actually observes employees as they work. During observation, the assessor notes whether employees are following safety and health procedures and if there are major safety and health violations.

The assessment process

Step 1: Thoroughly review all written safety and health documents.

Step 2: Conduct interviews with managers, supervisors and employees.

Step 3: Conduct job observations.

Types of assessments

Throughout the world, regulatory agencies have worked for years to develop assessment instruments that executives and safety professionals can use to measure safety initiatives. In addition, safety consulting firms and professionals have examined, refined and customized assessment instruments to meet a variety of organizational needs. As a result, when executives choose to conduct an assessment in their company, they have a variety of instruments from which to choose.

Total system assessment

A total system assessment enables executives to evaluate their entire safety management system. Using either a matrix or an assessment checklist, leaders assess their organization's effectiveness in every one of the nine elements of safety and health.

The following is an example of an assessment matrix. This particular matrix assesses Element 1: Management leadership and commitment. The left column lists the items executives need to assess, and the subsequent columns contain five levels of ratings. The person

Management leadership and commitment assessment matrix

Score Item	0 None	1 Poor	2 Fair	3 Good	4 Excellent
1 Written policy posted and disseminated	No written policy	Written policy, not promoted or disseminated.	Dissemination to some managers and supervisors.	Policy posted and disseminated. Managers & supervisors demonstrate knowledge of policy.	Evidence that management and employees support and advocate policy.
2 Safety management objectives	Program objectives have not been developed	Safety objectives developed as OSHA rates, not measured against OSHA recordables. Objectives developed but management not held accountable.	Activity objectives (JSA,JBO, etc.) developed, but not fully implemented or reviewed on a continuing basis.	Activity objectives given high priority by management.	Accountability in place.
3 Safety coordinator	No designation of safety coordinator.	Safety coordinator designated but limited management support	Safety coordinator is designated but other duties preclude accomplishing safety goals.	Safety coordinator is knowledgeable; basic program implemented; further compliance is needed.	Safety coordinator demonstrated proficiency in all aspects of the program. Acts as a resource for staff.
4 Accessibility/ organizational relationship with location management	No working relationship between safety coordinator and plant manager.	Safety coordinator reports to middle management. Limited management support.	Limited accessibility. No clearly defined organizational role, not considered part of management staff.	Good accessibility; roles defined. Mostly a verbal program; documentation needs improvement.	Close working relationship between coordinator and plant manager. Work together in collaborative and supportive mode.
5 Defined safety responsibilities	Responsibilities not assigned.	Management responsible for lowering "accidents". Limited understanding of safety management.	Verbal assignment of responsibility. Roles uncertain. No commitment to safety system is clear.	Roles and responsibilities established in writing. Limited commitment of time and personnel.	Clear commitment to adhere to policy and safety system. Evaluations performed to ensure needs are met.
6 Safety included in employee performance evaluation and salary review	Management does not use or consider safety performance in salary reviews.	"Safety" referenced in annual review but not measurable.	Review is on informal basis, for some personnel, at some times and may include safety "performance".	Safety activities goals developed and tracked by coordinator. Limited accountability for meeting goals	A formal program is used to evaluate safety activity performance. Safety performance included in review.

Source: National Safety Council

– or team – conducting the assessment should look at each item in the matrix and assign an appropriate score. Of course, for a system-wide assessment, leaders need to use one matrix for *each* of the nine safety and health system elements.

As its name implies, an assessment checklist is simply a list of the items the organization intends to assess. To use this list, assessors examine each item, and then indicate whether it is currently in place in the organization. The worksheets included at the end of each chapter in this book are examples of assessment checklists. Used together, they constitute a good template for a baseline assessment of all nine elements of safety and health.

If executives choose to use these checklists, they should refine each one to reflect their company's culture, policies and practices. As their safety management system matures, the questions on the list will change. Executives who are committed to safety should quickly progress beyond asking questions such as "Has a comprehensive series of baseline assessments been conducted at all organizational levels?" Once executives answer "yes" to that question, they need to move on to determine, for example, whether they have strategic plans based on assessment results or whether they have scheduled a follow-up series of assessments at all organizational levels.

Management assessment

As Element 1 demonstrated, there can be no safety management system unless senior executives lead the way. Therefore, one of the most critical factors an organization must assess is management commitment and support.

Most instruments that provide a comprehensive organizational assessment of safety and health also have a component evaluating management effectiveness. Although these instruments vary slightly on the items they include, most are in accordance with the findings of a study by the National Institute for Occupational Safety and Health (NIOSH). This study found that effective safety and health programs (as measured by incident rates) have a management team that conducts and supports the following activities:

- Give safety and health efforts high stature and commitment.
- Use outside influences to instill safety consciousness in the workforce.
- Use a variety of promotional and recognition techniques.
- Provide both general and specialized job safety training at the production level.
- Use a humanistic approach to disciplining those who violate safety rules and policies.
- Require formal inspections to supplement formal assessments.
- Use both engineering and non-engineering approaches to incident prevention.
- Develop a stable workforce.

In addition to evaluating the above, an assessor may use a formal instrument that examines management culture, practices and policies. The format of this instrument may range from a simple questionnaire to a more complex scored grid. Regardless of the format, its purpose is to determine which management practices are present that support safety and health programs and policies.

Executives and managers also should evaluate their safety commitment during performance evaluation. At the very least, they should establish a baseline by identifying which practices are in place, and then set goals to improve their commitment to, and implementation of, safety in their department.

Perception surveys

Safety management systems and programs are most effective when employees and managers at all levels perceive them as having value. Perception surveys evaluate the subjective factors influencing the safety management system – perceptions, attitudes and acceptance – in measurable terms.

Perception surveys assess employees' feelings about, and impressions of, the safety and health initiatives in the organization. They also pinpoint the gaps between perceptions at various levels of the organization. When administered periodically, perception surveys can determine the effects of new safety and health initiatives, as well as overall improvement or deterioration of system effectiveness. Furthermore, survey results complement observation and sampling by identifying employee attitudes that may be affecting safe job performance.

The perception survey instrument is a questionnaire distributed to employees at all levels of the organization. Usually, a third-party firm formulates, administers and analyzes the assessment. This firm also generates an assessment report, which provides information that senior leaders can use to develop strategies and mid-management performance objectives. Once executives have conducted an initial assessment, they can request follow-up surveys every 1 to 3 years, or when they implement significant program or cultural changes.

Who should conduct assessments

Executives have two choices when they conduct a comprehensive organizational assessment. They can form an internal team and perform a self-assessment, or they can hire someone from outside the organization and have a third-party assessment. To make the best choice, they should learn the benefits and drawbacks of each choice, then select the method that best meets the needs of their organization.

Self-assessments

Self-assessments are those that individuals or groups conduct from within the corporate structure. The evaluators can be professional staff or internal groups trained to conduct assessments.

Professional staff may come from the corporate, division or facility levels and may include safety professionals, occupational health professionals, risk managers or engineers. Internal groups may be safety committees, safety circles, operations teams or other task forces. All individuals within the corporate structure – managers, supervisors, line employees, labor representatives, maintenance and engineering personnel – can participate in the assessment process as long as they are qualified to do so.

Organizations enjoy several advantages when conducting self-assessments. First, internal employees have a better working knowledge of the organization than do outside consultants. Because employees are familiar with corporate culture and operations, and because they are more likely to have a working knowledge of operations within the organization, they also are more likely to be aware of key safety issues and their underlying root causes. Moreover, employees become aware of organizational and procedural changes as they occur, so they can conduct assessments without requiring a background briefing on organizational status.

Another advantage of self-assessment is that management retains more control regarding operational scheduling. When external consultants conduct assessments, they usually do so in a single, uninterrupted process that moves methodically and comprehensively through the organization. This can be disruptive to productivity. With self-assessments, employees can work in phases, and thereby present less disruption to productivity.

Self-assessment also augments employee involvement in two important ways. First, when line employees conduct assessments, they broaden their awareness of the organization's safety processes and practices. Second, self-assessment gives employees a voice in the decision-making process – one that reflects both their first-hand knowledge of operations and procedures and their ideas for solutions to safety and health problems.

Finally, self-assessment is the key to continuous improvement, which requires ongoing assessment. Because outside consultants are only available to work intermittently with an organization, they are unable to participate in comprehensive, continuing evaluation. Employees can fill in the gaps by assessing a process or practice as often as necessary.

If executives plan to have employees conduct self-assessments – and they should – they must provide the proper training. Employees who will be auditing the organization need in-depth training that includes learning not only the company operations and equipment, but also all the instruments required to complete the assessment process.

The instructors teaching the internal auditors should be professionals experienced in the audit process. Training should include both a classroom component as well as on-the-job observation in which trainees observe a professional doing several audits. Topics in the classroom training should include:

- The employee role in conducting assessments
- Procedures for conducting assessments
- Introduction to assessment forms and tools
- Procedures for creating an assessment report
- Procedures for following up after the assessment has ended

In addition, assessors should be competent in any skill or knowledge area applicable to the specific assessment instrument or type. This may include interviewing skills (qualitative assessments), hazard identification and analysis and priority development (technical audits), knowledge of regulatory standards (compliance audits), statistical validation procedures (sampling) and job safety analysis (observations).

Because of the wide variety of assessment instruments available to executives, it is impossible to describe all training required of an internal auditor. For each assessment tool executives choose for their organization, they should carefully examine necessary training for the employees who will be using the tool.

Third-party assessments

Third-party assessments are those performed by people from outside the organization, including representatives of regulatory agencies and private consulting firms. Executives might choose a third party to conduct a variety of assessments, including:

- Comprehensive assessments of the overall safety and health management system
- In-depth assessments of specific technical or compliance problem areas
- Special assessment processes, such as perception surveys, not easily handled by internal staff
- Informal compliance audits, including those that are required and voluntary

Third-party assessments are inherently more objective than internal processes. Because third parties are external to the organization, they are not as subject to influences such as organizational allegiance or internal politics. Moreover, because outsiders do not see an organization's systems and processes on a daily basis, they are less likely to miss the details of an operation that employees might take for granted.

Because third-party assessors have experience observing a wide variety of organizational cultures and programs, they bring a universal knowledge of what constitutes and supports a good safety and health system. This background is more likely to contribute to a thorough, accurate assessment than an internal assessor's expertise in any given area.

Because third parties offer objectivity and perspective, employees in an organization – from top management all the way to hourly employees – may view them as more credible. While this credibility may be partly a matter of perception, it nonetheless makes assessment findings and recommendations less threatening – and thus more readily accepted and implemented – by the recipients of the assessment.

When executives select a third party to assess their organization, they should look for a number of factors including familiarity with regulatory requirements, industry experience, technical knowledge of the processes that will be assessed and assessment experience. In the case of a compliance-based inspection, the assessor must have knowledge of regulatory requirements. With all other assessments, executives can be more flexible in what they require. In some instances, they may want someone with a highly-specialized background. In other instances, they may find that broad experience in a variety of industries is more useful.

Executives should require third-party candidates to provide individual resumes and client references. They also should call the references to verify the third party has the experience and background to do the job.

Once they select an assessor, executives should prepare a contract summarizing their expectations. The contract should specify the following information:

- The type of assessment(s) to be performed
- The processes that will be audited
- How daily results should be summarized
- The standards for the final assessment report

When executives make it clear what they expect from their third-party assessor, they are more likely to get the best assessment results possible.

Assessment reports

Every assessment an organization performs – whether it is internal or through a third party – should conclude with a report to management. This report should provide the following information:

- A summary of the strengths and weaknesses in the safety management system
- A diagnosis of factors or situations that are causing problems, prioritized by likelihood of occurrence and loss potential
- A projection of when and where to expect problems
- Guidelines for remedy, including alternatives and interim corrective measures

Within 30 days of receiving the report, executives need to identify corrective action. They can then communicate the report results to everyone in the organization and inform them of the actions they intend to take.

All formal reports become corporate records. Reports reinforce memory and provide a basis for comparing subsequent evaluations.

Follow up

Top managers need to do more than simply identify corrective actions. They also must budget for and schedule time to complete the actions, and then ensure the appropriate people follow through. The action plan they create should clearly identify the needed corrections, the people responsible for making them and the target dates for completion. The plan also should specify when top management will follow up to ensure the corrections have been made.

In addition to correcting specific hazards identified in the report, executives should realize that a single problem in one department might be symptomatic of an organization-wide problem. For this reason, top managers should consider applying their corrective action throughout the organization – not just in the area where the assessor found the problem. By doing this, executives will systematically eliminate not just the problem identified by the assessor, but all related problems as well.

Voluntary regulatory assessments

Organizations needing assistance in identifying and correcting hazards or in developing educational programs can contact OSHA for help. OSHA offers free comprehensive consultation services that provide the following:

- Appraisal of hazards, work practices and/or corporate programs
- Assistance in the implementation of agency recommendations
- Follow-up inspections to ensure organizations make the required corrections

The OSHA personnel who conduct these assessments are not compliance officers; however, if an organization fails to correct the noted hazards that fall within OSHA's jurisdiction, the consultant will refer the matter for enforcement action.

Non-abatement and consequent enforcement referral is rare; businesses that request assistance are usually committed to effective safety and health management. More often than not, the organization complies with cited OSHA requirements within the period allowed for hazard correction. OSHA grants a one-year exemption from programmed OSHA inspections to those businesses requesting comprehensive evaluations, correcting identified hazards and implementing safety and health programs meeting OSHA's requirements.

Voluntary Protection Programs
OSHA's Voluntary Protection Programs (VPP) foster a cooperative relationship between management, labor and OSHA. Approved VPP facilities must do one of the following:
- Design and implement safety and health programs that meet all 051-IA criteria for effective safety and health management (Star Program)
- Demonstrate potential and willingness to achieve Star status (Merit Program)
- Demonstrate alternate approaches to safety and health management that meet the purposes of Star criteria (Demonstration Program)

Interested organizations must complete a self-assessment checklist as the initial step toward VPP participation. Once OSHA approves an organization's application, non-enforcement personnel visit the site to conduct a document review, a facility walk-through and formal interviews. When OSHA approves candidates for VPP, it publicly designates them as participants in the appropriate program category, and removes them from programmed inspection lists; however, organizations must still maintain compliance with VPP's high standards, and to ensure they do, OSHA periodically reassesses them.

Executives should seriously consider getting involved with VPP or similar voluntary programs. The sustained benefits of participation – improved morale and motivation, community recognition, program improvement and continued cooperative assistance – far outweigh any temporary start-up disadvantages. At the very least, the internal and external assessments required for the application process can contribute significantly to an organization's assessment system.

Conducting audits

A safety and health audit is a comprehensive and systematic review of an organization's operations to determine how well managers, supervisors and employees are conforming

Element 3.2

Management establishes formal policy and procedures for periodic audits.

to established safety standards, guidelines and practices. Executives should include an audit policy in the organization's overall safety and health policy. The business plan and the organization's safety and health priorities drive the design for the audit system, which is preventive in nature and focuses on audits that are most likely to expose hazards and unsafe conditions. Employees at all levels of the organization participate and give input into the development of the audit system. The audit policy should include the following components:

Element 3.2.1
Element 3.2.2
Element 3.2.3
Element 3.2.4
Element 3.2.5
Element 3.2.6
Element 3.2.7

- A summary of the types of audits that should be conducted
- The scope and purpose of each audit
- Defined roles, responsibilities, qualifications and competencies of team members
- A schedule for the various types of audits
- Standards and procedures for conducting the audits
- Observations, findings and management response
- A program review of one or all of the elements of the safety management system

Types of audits

When leaders plan the audit system for their organization, they will have a variety of tools and instruments from which to choose. There are audits available to assess virtually every safety-related practice and process in the organization including:

- Adherence to safety policy
- Incident investigation reports
- Records of inspection and examination of equipment
- Safe operating procedures for various operations
- Electrical/mechanical safeguarding
- Results of industrial hygiene surveys
- Facility emergency plans
- Material Safety Data Sheet compliance
- OSHA injury and illness record keeping
- Inspection procedures and schedules
- Job safety analysis procedures and schedules
- Job safety observation procedures and schedules
- Safety budget
- Safety education and training

To determine the types of audits to be used, executives should review their business plan and stated safety and health priorities. They also should seek input from employees at all levels of the organization to learn the safety priorities. Once they have gathered sufficient information, they can select a battery of audits that will help them determine the effectiveness of their safety and health policies and practices. The following sections describe some of the most common types of audits.

Safety and health inspection

A safety and health inspection is a formal and thorough examination of the equipment and processes in the workplace. Effective safety and health inspections focus on fact finding, not fault finding. The goal is to ensure a safe work environment by detecting existing and potential hazards; then correcting them before an incident occurs.

Using a safety inspection checklist, the inspector goes to a work area and reviews the working conditions. The inspector's job is to identify positive safety factors as well as items for improvement. An inspector should inform employees if they are performing a procedure incorrectly and putting themselves at risk.

Afterward, the reviewer writes an inspection report. The report highlights the department's positive practices, points out areas needing improvement and suggests corrective actions. The department, in turn, makes the corrections to create a safer workplace.

Job safety observation

Job safety observation is the process of observing employees as they complete their work. The purpose is to recognize and reinforce safe job performance, to intervene when there are gaps in safe performance, and to elicit employee input on how the job can be safer. In some organizations, managers and supervisors conduct the observations; in other organizations, employees do the observing. It is also possible for an organization to use both supervisors and employees as observers.

Using a safety observation checklist, the observer watches an employee doing a job or a part of a job, then determines if the employee is performing the job according to safe operating procedures. Afterward, the observer gives the employee feedback on activities the employee did safely as well as those that were at-risk. The observer also writes up an observation report and works with the employee to identify corrective action. An example of a safety observation checklist is shown on the next page.

Sampling

Sampling is the process of touring a facility and recording the number of safe and at-risk factors. Trained observers conduct sampling at random – yet regular – intervals, and use the information gathered to calculate safety trends in the organization. Managers and supervisors then analyze these trends to determine corrective action.

During sampling, observers evaluate employees using a form that lists specific standard practices. They record safe and at-risk practices, and then calculate the total of safe practices as a percentage of all observations (both safe and at-risk). Sampling is by no means an assessment of the overall safety management system, but it gives managers a direct and short-term "snapshot" of employee safety behavior.

To set up a valid sampling system, executives will need some training or the assistance of a statistician. Once the system is set up, however, anyone can easily use it to accomplish ongoing evaluation of work practices.

Sample safety observation checklist

Observer: _____ **Task:** _____ **Date:** _____

Record safe practices with an "S," at-risk practices an "AR"

Environment
- __ Housekeeping
- __ Hazardous materials
- __ Lighting
- __ Noise
- __ Temperature
- __ Ventilation

Work Practices
- __ JSA exist?
- __ JSA followed?
- __ Procedures exist?
- __ Procedures followed?
- __ Procedures compatible with task

Equipment & Tools
- __ Correct for the job?
- __ Used correctly?
- __ Properly managed?
- __ Machine guards exist?
- __ Machine guards used?

PPE
- __ Head gear
- __ Eye & face protection
- __ Ear protection
- __ Hand & arm protection
- __ Leg & foot protection
- __ Respiratory protection

Chemical Hazards
- __ Inhalation
- __ Skin contact
- __ Absorption
- __ Injection
- __ Ingestion

Physical Hazards
- __ Electrical
- __ Fire/explosion
- __ Radiation
- __ Thermal stress
- __ Caught in/on/between
- __ Pinch points
- __ Struck against
- __ Struck by

Biological Hazards
- __ Bloodborne pathogens
- __ Brucellosis
- __ Building-related illness
- __ Legionnaires' disease
- __ Plant/insect poisons
- __ Tuberculosis (TB)
- __ Water & wastewater

Ergonomic Hazards
- __ Repetition
- __ Forceful exertions
- __ Awkward postures
- __ Contact stress
- __ Vibration
- __ Work area design

Discussion Items

1. How are the safety procedures we have in place working?

2. What concerns do you have about safety on the job?

3. How could your job be made easier?

4. What are the areas where we should provide safety training?

5. Are you comfortable with how everyone in the department follows safety procedures?

6. What would you do if you saw a co-worker violating a safety policy or procedure?

Commendable Items

_____
_____
_____
_____
_____
_____
_____
_____
_____
_____

Improvement Items

_____
_____
_____
_____
_____
_____
_____
_____
_____
_____

Follow-up Items

_____
_____
_____
_____
_____
_____
_____
_____
_____
_____

Total # of safe behaviors_____   **Total # of at-risk behaviors**_____

OSHA record keeping

The OSHA record keeping system mandates employers to record and report work-related illnesses, injuries, and fatalities; and to prepare a summary once a year. Employers must post this summary in a visible location so employees can learn about the injuries and illnesses occurring in their workplace.

Some executives may grumble at having to maintain such an extensive record-keeping system simply to satisfy OSHA. Most likely, these executives will do the minimum amount of work to keep the records and post the results. On the other hand, safe-minded and smart executives will recognize the OSHA system is an important component of their overall safety management system. They will not only keep the required records and prepare the required report; they also will analyze the records for trends, hold meetings with employees regarding the report, and make improvements in their system based on the report. Furthermore, they will integrate the OSHA record-keeping system into a larger and more comprehensive safety management system.

Continuous improvement

Once an organization has performed the necessary system-wide assessments and audits, identified corrections and completed the required corrective actions, the safety and health system should show significant improvement. This is because the organization has based their system on the principles of continuous improvement, which is the process of constantly assessing all nine of the safety and health elements and taking action to improve them.

Element 3.3

The safety management system is based on the principles of continuous improvement.

The continuous improvement model

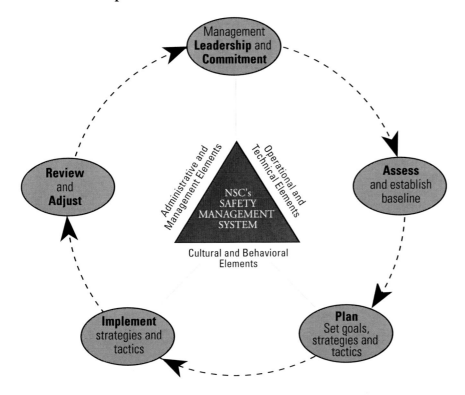

Element 3.3.1

Management commitment to and leadership of, the continuous improvement process

Element No. 1 emphasizes the fact that no safety and health system can be effective unless it has management support and commitment. The same is true for continuous improvement. Top management must drive the effort. Without commitment from the top, no one else in the organization will be committed either. On the other hand, if executives lead the way, employees will be more likely to embrace and support continuous improvement.

Element 3.3.2

Assessing the current situation and identifying the issues using the nine elements as a guide

Assessment is an important part of continuous improvement. An organization needs to know how well its safety and health system is working before it can determine how to make it better. A baseline measurement helps executives know where to focus their efforts.

Element 3.3.3

Planning measurable improvement goals, strategies and tactics

Once executives know the status of their safety and health systems, they can create a plan for improvement. Effective safety culture never happens by chance. Leaders must build it into their business plans by setting safety-related goals, strategies and tactics.

Element 3.3.4

Implementing the plans

Plans are a good start for improving safety and health systems, but unless an organization implements them, they are ineffective. Executives need to make it clear to everyone in the organization that carrying out safety and health plans is just as important as doing the production part of their jobs.

Element 3.3.5

Reviewing and adjusting the process to facilitate constant improvement

Once employees have completed their safety and health plans, they will need to review and adjust them. They need to learn what was effective, discard what was not effective, and identify new areas for improvement. Once they do this, they begin the continuous improvement process again.

Continuous improvement should be at the foundation of any safety management system. When executives consistently practice the five steps in the continuous improvement process, they will see constant improvement in safety and health within their organizations.

Element 3: Assessments, audits and continuous improvement review

Issues/questions	In place			Action plan (if "no" or "partially")
	Yes	No	Partially	
1. Does senior management regularly assess its safety and health strategies and goals? Are these self-assessments compared to other assessment results?				
2. Are a variety of assessment tools used in the company assessment program?				
3. Has a comprehensive baseline series of assessments been conducted at all organizational levels?				
4. Are assessments conducted at all company levels – corporate, division and facility?				
5. Does the overall assessment system include both internal and external assessment processes?				
6. Is the internal assessment staff trained by professionals? Have they accompanied a professional on an assessment?				
7. Are credentials and client references required of third-party assessors?				
8. Are standards and procedures established for assessment reporting and follow up?				
9. Does the organization conduct voluntary regulatory assessments?				
10. Does the organization have an audit policy and procedures that clearly explain the following: • A summary of the types of audits that should be conducted? • The scope and purpose of each audit? • Defined roles, responsibilities, qualifications and competencies of team members? • A schedule for the various types of audits? • Standards and procedures for conducting the audits? • Observations, findings and management response? • A program review of one or all of the elements of the safety management system?				

Element 3: Assessments, audits and continuous improvement review

Issues/questions	In place			Action plan (if "no" or "partially")
	Yes	No	Partially	
11. Does the organization use the continuous improvement process to constantly make the safety and health system better?				

element 4

hazard recognition,
evaluation and control

Element 4: Hazard recognition, evaluation and control

4.1 Management establishes and maintains a policy for ongoing recognition, evaluation and control or elimination of workplace hazards in order to maintain an acceptable level of risk in the workplace. The hazard control policy should establish:

    4.1.1 Written procedures to be used in identifying, analyzing and controlling hazards.

    4.1.2 A budget with sufficient funds for effective hazard control program implementation.

    4.1.3 The active involvement and participation of workers exposed to hazards as an essential element of the hazard control program.

    4.1.4 A reliable system that encourages employees to report hazards and concerns and that includes a method to follow up with employees.

4.2 Management establishes a hazard analysis procedure to identify existing and potential hazards, as well as conditions and operations in which changes might create hazards. Several tools may be used to do this based on organizational needs, capabilities and resources. These include: job safety analysis, safety inspections, risk assessments, industrial hygiene exposure assessments, incident investigations, process hazard analysis and system safety reviews. To implement a thorough analysis:

    4.2.1 Conduct a comprehensive, baseline survey for safety and health and periodic, comprehensive update surveys. Areas to be considered within the survey include: environment, including chemical, physical, biological and ergonomic hazards, as well as walking/working surfaces, lighting, temperature and ventilation; equipment and processes, including construction plans, tool/equipment conditions, housekeeping, and machine and electrical safeguards; and employee/management work practices, including use of personal protective equipment, appropriate equipment, tools and machines, safety devices, established safe work practices and proper lifting techniques.

    4.2.2 Perform routine job hazard analysis.

    4.2.3 Conduct periodic and daily safety and health inspections of the workplace.

    4.2.4 Include a change analysis of planned and new facilities, processes, materials, and equipment or when staffing changes occur.

    4.2.5 Review hazards found during worksite analysis to determine the safety system failure that caused the hazard. The system failure should then be corrected to ensure similar hazards do not reoccur.

    4.2.6 Document analysis results and enter into the record-keeping system.

4.3 Management will initiate a hazard evaluation or risk assessment process. The hazard evaluation system will assess risks according to probability of occurrences, severity of outcomes and employee exposure. The qualitative hazard probability should be determined through research, analysis and evaluation of historical safety data on similar systems.

4.3.1 Establish appropriate definitions of hazard severity, probability and exposure categories to establish understandable qualitative measures for incidents that might occur if a potential hazard is identified.

4.4 Management will ensure staff design and implement control measures when worker exposure to health or physical hazards is found to pose an unacceptable risk. The best practice approach is to eliminate hazards at the design stage. If not feasible, the following hierarchy of control measures should be applied:

4.4.1 Engineering controls should be used as the first and most reliable strategy to control a hazard at its source when workers are exposed to hazards.

4.4.2 Administrative controls can be used to minimize worker exposure through policies, procedures and rules such as standard operating procedures when engineering controls are not feasible.

4.4.3 Personal protective equipment can be used as a supplementary control method when exposure to hazards cannot be engineered out of the process and when administrative controls cannot provide sufficient protection. Use PPE when engineering and administrative controls are not feasible, as an interim control method while "higher" controls are being implemented, or as added protection. PPE should not be used as a substitute for engineering or administrative controls.

Overview

Occupational health and safety efforts involve the control and elimination of recognized workplace hazards to attain an acceptable level of risk and promote the wellness of workers. Controlling hazards requires a continuous proactive process of anticipating, identifying, designing, implementing and evaluating risk-reduction practices.

The first step in the process is identifying hazards. A hazard can be defined as any existing or potential workplace condition that, by itself or by interacting with other variables, can result in death, injury, property damage or other loss. Hazards include sub-standard conditions, practices and procedures. Before a hazard can be controlled, it must be recognized.

Once recognized, hazards must be evaluated and assessed according to risk. Risk can be defined as a measure of the probability and severity of adverse effects. Management may state a goal of "zero injuries," which is different than "zero risk." A zero-risk environment does not exist; simply sitting in a chair can involve risk. The goal is to reduce risk to an "acceptable" level. Risks are acceptable if judged to be tolerable. For any operation to succeed, risks must be acceptable. A risk assessment technique ranks risk by three criteria: exposure, consequence or severity, and probability. The information developed during the risk assessment guides effective management decision making.

The third step in the process is to control hazards or bring them within an acceptable level of risk.

Injuries and illnesses don't just happen, they are caused. Management must take proactive measures to find and fix hazards before they lead to injuries and illnesses. Element 4 addresses hazard recognition, evaluation and control.

Hazard recognition

Element 4.1

Management establishes and maintains a policy for ongoing recognition, evaluation and control or elimination of workplace hazards in order to maintain an acceptable level of risk in the workplace.

Recognizing and evaluating hazards is an ongoing task. Low incident and injury rates do not necessarily signify a hazard-free workplace. Management must look beyond any temporary absence of injuries or incidents and adopt a proactive approach. The emphasis in this approach is on prevention. As has been demonstrated time and again, hazards that cause no injury or result in a first-aid injury have the potential to result in a serious or disabling injury or illness in the future. In order to create an injury-free work environment, it is necessary to find and correct hazards before the potential for serious injury is realized.

There is no simple way to control hazards. Hazard control is the result of a continuous process involving identification, evaluation, planning, implementation and re-evaluation. Management must be committed to:

- Adopting the philosophy and mission of working toward zero incidents
- Endorsing the hazard control program
- Setting forth written procedures to control hazards
- Adhering to safe management practices
- Allocating sufficient funds to implement an effective hazard-control program

Management's commitment to control hazards must be followed by implementation. Successful implementation can be achieved by:
- Setting reachable goals
- Developing and implementing strategies and procedures to recognize, evaluate and control hazards
- Periodically reevaluating the program's effectiveness

Employees are the key to discovering and controlling hazards that may develop or already exist in the workplace. A reliable system for employee reporting is a critical part of the safety management system. Management should establish multiple ways to report hazards so that, depending on comfort level and nature of issues, there are several ways to address concerns. This could include the supervisor chain of command, health and safety committee member, voice mailbox or a suggestion box. It is necessary to ensure timely and appropriate responses to employees.

Employees should have the opportunity to be actively engaged in the aspects of the program dealing with the recognition, evaluation and control of hazards. This would include activities such as conducting safety inspections and job safety analysis and selecting personal protective equipment.

Worksite hazard analysis

Hazards must be identified to protect employees. A means of systematically identifying workplace hazards as they occur is needed so hazards can be eliminated before accidents occur. The greater number of ways problems are brought to management's attention, the less likely is it that an accident will occur when one of the reporting systems fails.

An effective worksite hazard analysis is one that is planned and well communicated. The following questions should be considered prior to conducting the analysis:
- What is the goal of this analysis – to proactively find improvements, to identify the cause of a problem, part of a routine job safety analysis?
- What will be analyzed – chemical, physical, biological or ergonomic hazards; all hazards; hazards pertaining to a specific job or injury?
- Who will be involved in the analysis – who will be conducting the analysis and who will be observed and interviewed?
- Which method of analysis will be used to get the best, most helpful results?
- How will workers be informed about the analysis – at a meeting, posted on a bulletin board, in an e-mail, through the company newsletter?

The following are types of worksite hazard analyses.
Comprehensive surveys
Comprehensive surveys should be performed by qualified individuals who have the knowledge, skills and experience to recognize and evaluate hazards that may be present in the workplace. Three general areas – the environment, equipment and processes, and employee and management practices – should be reviewed.

Element 4.2

Management establishes a hazard analysis procedure to identify existing and potential hazards, as well as conditions and operations in which changes might create hazards. Several tools may be used to do this based on organizational needs. These include: job safety analysis, safety inspections, risk assessments, industrial hygiene exposure assessments, incident investigations, process hazard analysis and system safety reviews.

Element 4.2.1

Conduct a comprehensive baseline safety and health survey and periodic update surveys.

The environment includes chemical, physical, biological and ergonomic hazards, as well as walking and working surfaces, lighting, temperature and ventilation. Equipment and processes include construction plans, tool and equipment conditions, housekeeping, and machine and electrical safeguards. Employee and management work practices include use of personal protective equipment, appropriate equipment, tools and machines, safety devices, established safe work practices and proper lifting techniques.

Industrial hygiene exposure assessments
Preventing hazardous chemical and physical agent exposures is one goal of industrial hygiene assessments. Industrial hygienists should be involved in purchasing new equipment and planning processes and facilities to prevent these exposures.

Some existing work environments expose employees to potentially harmful levels of substances or forms of energy. Overexposure to harmful substances or energy sources – such as noise, vibration, heat, cold, and ionizing or non-ionizing radiation – may cause injury or illness in employees. These injuries or illnesses may be observed shortly after exposure (acute effects) or only after a long period of exposure (chronic, or long-term, effects).

It is crucial to determine exposure levels and to identify ways to reduce exposures. Industrial hygiene exposure assessments identify specific agents to which employees may be exposed and evaluate the possible impact on employee health. Exposure assessment results also are maintained for medical purposes as well as for compliance with regulatory requirements in the United States.

The assessment yields recommendations on ways to reduce or eliminate worker exposure. Industrial hygiene exposure assessments should be conducted by qualified, professional industrial hygienists and require special equipment and, often, complicated procedures to sample and measure the levels of substances in the work environment.

Industrial hygiene exposure assessments are conducted by gathering data on the nature of the chemicals used and on workplace levels of hazardous substances. The data can be gathered using several techniques, including personal, environmental, biological and medical monitoring and reviews of Material Safety Data Sheets and process flows.

Data evaluation covers such factors as the level and duration of exposure and the toxicity of the substance. In the United States, OSHA has established standards for many of the most hazardous substances. The standards outline permissible exposure limits to which employees can be exposed on a daily basis.

Element 4.2.2
Perform routine job hazard analysis

Routine job hazard analysis
Job hazard analysis – also called job safety analysis (JSA) – is a systematic method of hazard recognition and evaluation. JSA considers each work task as a series of steps, each with its own hazards.

JSA identifies the hazards associated with each step and identifies ways to eliminate or protect against them. JSAs are a series of written procedures for eliminating, minimizing and protecting against the hazards associated with particular jobs and their tasks. JSAs help:

58

- Standardize work practices by identifying and specifying individual job-task steps
- Establish a framework for evaluating adherence to safe and efficient work practices
- Create hazard awareness by the continuing focus on prevention
- Reduce the number of injuries, illnesses and incidents
- Identify causes of incidents that occur

Other, more sophisticated, techniques are necessary when complex risks are involved. Such techniques include What-If Checklist, Failure Mode and Effect Analysis, Hazard and Operability Study and Fault Tree Analysis.

Health and safety inspection

A health and safety inspection is a thorough examination of the workplace to ensure a safe work environment by detecting existing and potential hazards so they can be corrected before an incident occurs.

Inspections are conducted to identify unsafe practices, procedures and processes. Employees and supervisors should monitor their areas and equipment on an ongoing basis to identify and correct hazardous situations. If a hazard is observed, it is important to report the problem quickly and follow up with corrective action. A continuous, ongoing inspection program will aid in early identification and correction of hazardous conditions and may prevent serious injury or other loss.

Planned inspections at intervals provide a way to monitor the effectiveness of the physical aspects of the entire safety and health program. Inspections should be used in connection with other hazard identification and evaluation techniques.

There are several types of planned inspections, which may be conducted either on a scheduled basis or intermittently. The inspection techniques will depend on the type of industry and the specific situation. A separate written procedure should be developed for each type of inspection. For example, records, equipment and production process inspections may each require individual procedures.

Each written procedure should establish a timetable. The procedure should identify the job function of the individuals responsible for conducting the inspection, the subjects to be inspected, inspection format and guidelines for reporting, communication of results and follow-up. The written procedure also should include an inspection checklist and sample forms for reporting hazards.

Inspections are conducted by observing and comparing work practices with standard operating procedures, observing physical facilities and examining equipment, preventive maintenance and other records to ensure compliance. Inspections should be conducted by people who are experienced and trained in hazard identification. Inspectors may include safety, health or industrial hygiene personnel, managers, supervisors or line employees. All inspectors should be familiar with the processes and practices so they can identify hazards.

Generally, inspection frequency will depend on the potential for loss of property, casualty or business interruption. For example, a large manufacturing facility using

Element 4.2.3
Conduct periodic and daily safety and health inspections of the workplace.

59

hazardous raw materials will require more frequent and detailed inspections than a small business office. However, there may be other factors, such as regulatory and insurance requirements, dictating the frequency of inspections.

Inspections can yield much information with respect to weaknesses and areas needing improvement. Inspections are valuable in determining the direction of the hazard control program and in setting new program goals and strategies. It is crucial to implement corrective measures as soon as possible and follow up on the implementation process. Subsequent inspections will demonstrate the effectiveness of the follow-up.

Inspection results should be included in a formal report submitted to management. The report should cover the status of the hazard control program and areas for improvement, as well as recommended corrective actions. Management is ultimately accountable for safety performance and must be involved in steps to improve that performance. In addition, management controls resource allocations, and the inspection results may indicate a need for additional resources, such as additional safety and health training programs, a larger staff, redesign of a process or the purchase of equipment.

Careful records of the inspection should be maintained. The baseline defined by the inspection will be used to measure improvement in the hazard control process. Written records are subject to the right of discovery in the event of litigation; therefore, they should present only facts, not suppositions or guesses. Reports should focus on determining facts and recommending actions.

Safety observation tour

The safety observation tour is a part of the inspection process. It is personal interaction with employees to observe and discuss on-the-job safety performance and answer any questions.

Element 4.2.4
Conduct a change analysis of planned and new facilities, processes, materials and equipment or when staffing changes occur.

Change analysis

Anytime something new enters into a workplace – such as a new process, different materials, a new piece of equipment or new building – new hazards may unintentionally be introduced. Before considering such changes, analyze them thoroughly to help prevent problems before they develop.

Having a team of operators, engineers, and safety and health professionals jointly analyze potential changes or new equipment before they are put online can identify safety and production concerns up front, hopefully heading off problems before they develop. Fixing potential problems before they occur usually is less expensive than attempting to fix a problem after the fact. You may find change analysis useful in the following situations:
- Building or leasing a new facility
- Installing new equipment
- Using new materials
- Implementing new processes
- Changing staff

System Safety Reviews

Work operations are often considered as a system of interdependent processes and parts. The system parts must interact in a specified way in order to accomplish the desired end product. Businesses commonly evaluate these operational systems to identify potential failures, inefficiencies or other potential production problems. This systems approach also can be applied to hazard identification, evaluation and control. By using the techniques, such as inspection and job safety analysis, it is possible to identify safety or health hazards, and the potential for exposure to the hazards, within the production system. Ideally, a systems safety review should be performed at the design or conceptual phase so the potential for hazards can be addressed before the system goes online.

Determine Root Causes

After hazards are identified, they must be evaluated to determine their causes and their impact on workplace safety and health. Failure to identify the causes will result in failure to correct the hazard.

It is not enough to address the obvious visible hazard. It also is important to identify the main underlying problem or issue – the root cause. The root cause is defined as "the conditions or events, which, if eliminated or modified, will prevent an incident from recurring." In other words, finding and eliminating the root cause of a hazard is finding a permanent solution.

The 5-Why Analysis

One method you can use to find the root cause is the 5-Why Analysis. Here is how it works:

- The person conducting the investigation asks a series of questions, each beginning with the word "why."
- The first question is always "Why did the incident occur?"
- A person with the appropriate knowledge and expertise responds to the question.
- The investigator then says, "Why did that happen?"
- Once again, the expert answers.
- This goes on until the answer provided is one that can't be justified or explained.

This final inexplicable answer is most likely the root cause of the problem. The root cause doesn't always come up after five questions; it may take three, six or more questions. The idea is to ask "why" as many times as necessary until the root cause is discovered.

Incident investigation

Incident investigation is a tool for uncovering hazards missed earlier or those that slipped by planned controls. It is only useful when the process is positive and focuses on finding the root cause versus looking for someone to blame.

Management should investigate all incidents including "near misses." A slight change in time or position could have changed a near miss into an injury or damage.

Element 4.2.5

Review hazards found during worksite analysis to determine what failure in the safety system permitted the hazard to occur. The system failure should then be corrected to ensure similar hazards do not recur. In other words, find and eliminate the root cause of the problem.

Six key questions should be answered in an investigation report: who, what, when, where, why and how. Further, thorough interviews with everyone involved are necessary.

The primary purpose of the investigation is to prevent future occurrences. Results of the investigation should be used to initiate corrective action.

Trend analysis

Tracking injury and illness trends through time may identify patterns with common causes that can be prevented. Since there must be enough information for patterns to emerge, small sites may require a review of 3-5 years of records. Larger sites may find useful trends yearly, quarterly or monthly. When analyzing injury and illness records, look for similar injuries and illnesses. These generally indicate a lack of hazard controls. Look for the location of the injury or illness, the type of work that was being conducted, the time of day or type of equipment. Review of OSHA injury and illness forms is the most common form of pattern analysis, but other records of hazards can be analyzed. Examples include inspection and employee hazard reporting records.

Hazard recognition: Categories/types of hazards

Hazards may be categorized by four types: chemical, physical, biological and ergonomic.

Chemical hazards	Physical hazards
Inhalation	Electrical
Skin contact	Fire/explosion
Absorption	Noise
Injection	Radiation
Ingestion	Thermal stress
	Caught in/on/between pinch points
	Slips/falls
	Striking against
	Struck by
Biological hazards	**Ergonomic hazards**
Bloodborne pathogens	Repetition
Brucellosis	Forceful exertions
Building-related illness	Awkward postures
Legionnaires' Disease	Contact stress
Mold	Vibration
Plant and insect poisons	Work area design
Tuberculosis	Tool or equipment design
Water and wastewater	

Chemical hazards result from excessive airborne concentrations of mists, vapors, gases or solids in the form of dusts or fumes. Chemicals may enter the body through inhalation, skin contact, absorption, injection and ingestion. If a chemical lacks a route of entry into the body, no harm will come to an individual. To prevent chemical incidents, identify and control routes of entry. Locate hazards by assessing workplaces and processes, including:

- Chemicals used as raw materials
- By-products that are manufactured
- Products that are manufactured
- By-products of the manufacturing process

Physical hazards include excessive noise levels, vibration, radiation, temperature extremes and exposure to electrical current. Also included are slips, trips and falls, as well as being stuck by or striking against other objects. Physical hazards can have immediate effects – such as a broken bone resulting from a fall – and cumulative health effects, such as hearing loss from long term exposure to noise.

Biological hazards result when a living organism or its properties cause an adverse response in humans. Biological hazards in the workplace come from agents such as infectious microorganisms, allergens and toxins.

An ergonomic hazard refers to a mismatch between a worker's physical capacity and the design of a work area, equipment, tools or physical demands of the job. An ergonomically-related musculoskeletal disorder of the soft tissues – muscles, nerves, tendons, ligaments, joints, cartilage, blood vessels and spinal discs – is caused by frequency and exposure to certain risk factors. Other hazards may result from work area design or tool/equipment design problems.

What to look for during a worksite analysis

What you look for in a worksite analysis will depend on your goals. Following is a list of common items that are reviewed.

Overall environment	Workstation design
<ul><li>Lighting</li><li>Noise</li><li>Temperature</li><li>Humidity</li></ul>	<ul><li>Control and display design</li><li>Location and orientation of work surfaces</li><li>Chair design</li><li>Task/Job design</li></ul>
Movements and repetions	**Machinery and equipment design**
<ul><li>Force</li><li>Vibration</li><li>Postural demands</li><li>Physical demands</li><li>Work pace</li><li>Tool design</li><li>Size and shape of work objects</li><li>Weight of work equipment and objects</li></ul>	<ul><li>Movement required to operate</li><li>Force required to operate</li><li>Vibration</li><li>Postural demands</li><li>Pace required to keep up with equipment</li></ul>

Materials handling	Accessibility
• Movements and repetitions • Postural demands • Physical demands • Size and shape of materials being handled • Weight of materials being handled	• Necessity to reach (up and/or out) • Other objects in the way

Guarding and warnings	
• Proper guards and warnings on equipment • Proper procedures in place	

Element 4.3

Management will initiate a hazard evaluation (risk assessment) process. The hazard evaluation system will evaluate and assess risks presented by hazard according to probability of occurrences, severity of outcomes and employee exposure. The qualitative hazard probability should be determined through research, analysis and evaluation of historical safety data on similar systems

Risk assessment method for rating hazards

Upon completion of the worksite hazard analysis, it is important to rank the most critical hazards. Which hazards should be acted upon immediately? Which can be acted upon at a later date? A risk assessment ranking examines hazards using three criteria:

Severity – how dire the consequences would be if the hazard caused an incident.

Exposure – how many employees are exposed to the hazard, and how many times they are exposed.

Probability – how likely it is that the hazard will result in an incident.

Severity can be measured on a four-point scale. The higher the number, the more serious the consequences.

Rating	Severity	Description
1	Negligible	Not likely to produce an injury, illness, lost production or lost workday.
2	Marginal	Might cause minor injury or illness, or minor property damage.
3	Critical	Likely to cause severe injury or illness, major property damage, significant lost work time, but not a permanent disability or fatality.
4	Catastrophic	Likely to cause permanent disability, loss of life, loss of facility or major environmental impact.

Exposure can be measured on a three-point scale. Assign a rating based on the total number of occurrences whether it is by number of employees, number of occurrences or both.

Rating	Exposure	Description
1	Minimal	A few employees perform the task up to a few times a day.
2	Moderate	A few employees perform the task frequently, or many employees perform the task occasionally.
3	High	Many employees perform the task frequently.

Probability also can be measured on a three-point scale. Assign a rating based on the likelihood the hazard will cause an incident to occur.

Rating	Probability	Description
1	Minimal	Unlikely that this hazard will cause an incident.
2	Moderate	Moderately likely that this hazard will cause an incident.
3	High	Highly likely that this hazard will cause an incident.

The ratings for severity, exposure and probability are added together to form a risk assessment priority rating.

Severity score: Exposure score:

Probability score: Total score:

Using the total score, the chart below prioritizes hazards

Points	Priority Rating	Description
10	Emergency	This situation must be handled immediately—no delays!
8-9	Extremely important	This situation needs to be handled today.
6-7	Very important	This situation needs to be handled within a week.
4-5	Somewhat important	This situation needs to be handled within a month.
3	Least important	This situation should be handled within three months.

Note: This rating scale is intended to be a guide only. It is not intended to be an absolute measurement system.

Source: National Safety Council

Element 4.4

Management will ensure that staff develop and implement control measures when worker exposure to health or physical hazards is found to pose an unacceptable risk. The best practice approach is to eliminate hazards at the design stage. If this is not feasible, then the hierarchy of control measures should be applied.

Control of workplace hazards

After prioritization, hazards must be corrected through implementation of appropriate controls – engineering, administrative or personal protective equipment.

For each hazard, ask, "What must be done to eliminate or control the hazard? Does equipment need to be refitted or replaced? Are better operating procedures needed? Is retraining required?" After the appropriate measures are identified, they must be implemented and reevaluated to determine their effectiveness in eliminating or controlling the hazard.

When worker exposure to health or physical hazards is found to pose a risk to employee safety, a control program must be implemented. The control methods chosen depend on the:

- Specific hazard
- Magnitude of exposure
- Effectiveness
- Available technology

Element 4.4.1

Engineering controls should be used as the first and most reliable strategy to control a hazard at its source.

Engineering controls

The first and most reliable strategy is to control a hazard at its source and design it out of the process. Engineering controls do this, unlike other controls that generally focus on an employee exposed to the hazard. The basic premise behind engineering controls is that, to the extent possible, the work environment and job must be designed to eliminate hazards or reduce exposure to hazards. If hazards cannot be eliminated, engineering controls often reduce them.

Today, companies are more likely than in the past to examine all possible ways to engineer out hazards. The cost of toxic materials disposal, health care, and workers' compensation is high. It is more cost effective to eliminate hazards and engineer safety into the design instead of at the time a hazard arises.

Some examples of designing facilities, equipment or processes so the hazard is no longer present are:

- Redesigning, changing or substituting equipment to remove the source of excessive temperature, noise or pressure
- Redesigning a process to use less toxic chemicals
- Redesigning a workstation to relieve physical stress and remove ergonomic hazards
- Designing general ventilation with sufficient fresh outdoor air to improve indoor air quality and generally to provide a safe, healthful atmosphere

When you cannot remove a hazard and cannot replace it with a less hazardous alternative, the next best control is enclosure. While this may control employee exposure during production, it may not control exposures during maintenance. Some examples of enclosure designs are:

- Complete enclosure of moving parts of machinery.

- Complete containment of toxic liquids or gasses throughout the entire process to detoxification, safe packing for shipment or safe disposal of toxic waste products.
- Glove box operations to enclose work with dangerous micro-organisms, radio nuclides or toxic substances.
- Complete containment of noise, heat or pressure.

When the potential hazard cannot be removed, replaced or enclosed, the next best approach is a barrier to exposure, or, in the case of air contaminants, local exhaust ventilation to remove the air contaminant from the workplace. This engineered control involves potential exposure to the worker even in normal operations, consequently, it should be used only in conjunction with other types of controls; such as safe work practices designed specifically for the site condition and/or personal protective equipment. Examples include:

- Ventilation hoods in laboratory work
- Machine guarding, including electronic barriers
- Duct away chemicals and noise
- Baffles used as noise-absorbing barriers
- Improve the lighting

Other types of engineering controls include:

- Improve heating/air conditioning
- Provide temperature/humidity control
- Make workstations adjustable to accommodate a range of people's sizes.
- Substitute equipment to minimize force, compression or vibration (for example, use low-speed sanding instead of grinding).
- Create operating controls that are clear, easy to read and readily accessible.
- Replace or adjust worn machine parts.
- Confine high-noise machines to insulated rooms.
- Install shades or blinds to eliminate glare.
- Automate a process to eliminate exposure to dangerous hand tools.

Administrative controls

Administrative controls minimize worker exposure to hazards by using policies, procedures and rules, such as standard operating procedures. This type of control is normally used with other controls that more directly prevent or control exposure to the hazard. Examples include:

- **Housekeeping.** Try to get individual workers to view housekeeping as part of their day-to-day job – not just as an extra task. Practice proper chemical storage procedures, as well as daily cleaning and organization. When done well, housekeeping can reduce incidents, improve morale, and increase efficiency and effectiveness.

Element 4.4.2

Administrative controls can be used to minimize worker exposure through policies, procedures and rules, such as standard operating procedures when engineering controls are not feasible.

- **Education/training.** Educate and train employees on safe job practices, hazard recognition and control methods.
- **Relief workers/rotation of workers.** Rotate employees in and out of jobs for relief in challenging work environments.
- **Breaks.** Set up break schedules that complement challenges faced in a job or work setting.
- **Warnings.** Create warnings for hazardous processes and substances. Create operating controls that are clear, easy to read and readily accessible.

Examples of administrative controls include:
- Conduct noise monitoring.
- Keep thorough records.
- Provide education and training on the proper use of tools and equipment.
- Provide stress-reduction training.
- Provide adequate work-rest periods.
- Provide job rotation to minimize the amount of time employees spend on a particular tool or piece of equipment.
- Inspect equipment and tools regularly.

Medical management: An administrative control

Medical management is an administrative control used to prevent and control work-related musculoskeletal disorders using all available health care resources. There are three phases to such medical management.

Phase 1: Prevention

The goal of prevention programs is to prevent any injury from occurring. Five factors to consider when setting up a prevention program are:

1. Develop and implement prevention plans such as job safety analysis, safety inspections and incident prevention.
2. Have detailed job descriptions that meet the Americans with Disabilities Act requirements.
3. Job descriptions should clearly define the physical requirements of every job.
4. Have baseline measurements, which allow monitoring progress toward injury prevention.
5. Have a job suggestion program. Encourage employees to suggest ways to improve ergonomic safety on the job.

Phase 2: Early intervention

Early intervention takes place immediately after an injury occurs. Its goal is to minimize sick time and to help employees return to work using early diagnosis and treatment. The steps to early intervention are:

1. Seek appropriate treatment.
2. Be aware of the symptoms, but don't diagnose. Refer employee to a professional.
3. Do not discriminate or retaliate – it is illegal to do so.
4. Maintain contact with the employee and the health care provider.
5. Get specific goals and time frames for recovery.
6. Modify the job duties so the employee can safety return to work.

Phase 3: Chronic injury

Chronic injury occurs after an injury. The goal is to prevent total disability and to help employees return to work by managing the condition. The steps are:

1. Get the injured worker re-evaluated.
2. Re-evaluation should include the worker, the health care providers, the claims manager, the employer, the occupational/physical therapist and the psychologist, if applicable.
3. This team should address every factor preventing the injured worker from returning to work.
4. Use the above information to create a plan for the employee. Options include:
   a. Return to work in a job that meets reduced capacity.
   b. Independent medical examination
   c. Functional/physical capacities evaluation
   d. Vocational rehabilitation assessment
   e. Psychological evaluation
   f. Work-hardening program
   g. Pain clinic program
   h. Total disability, as a last resort

Personal protective equipment

When exposure to hazards cannot be engineered completely out of normal operations or maintenance work, and when administrative controls cannot provide sufficient additional protection, a supplementary method of control is the use of personal protective clothing or equipment.

Personal protective equipment – such as respirators, gloves and safety glasses – are those articles of clothing or equipment worn by workers for protection. Such equipment does not reduce hazards, but provides a barrier between the worker and the hazard. If the decision is made to use only personal protective equipment to protect employees, it should be made after exhausting other controls or while engineering controls are being implemented.

Note: For specific OSHA requirements on personal protective equipment, see OSHA standard, 1910 Subpart I.

Personal protective equipment controls include:

- Provide eye protection, such as goggles and safety glasses.
- Encourage employees to wear extra clothing to reduce the effects of cold.

Element 4.4.3.

Personal protective equipment can be used as a supplementary control method when exposure to hazards cannot be engineered out and when administrative controls cannot provide sufficient protection. Use personal protective equipment when engineering and administrative controls are not feasible, as an interim control method while "higher" controls are being implemented, or as added protection. Personal protective equipment should not be used as a substitute for engineering or administrative controls.

69

- Provide items that absorb the impact of force, compression or vibration, such as gloves and insulation.
- Provide personal heat/cold packs.
- Provide footwear.
- Provide kneepads to prevent prolonged contact with hard or sharp surfaces.
- Provide head protection, such as hard hats and bump caps.
- Provide earplugs.
- Provide respirators – either air purifying or air supplied.
- Provide protective vests.

Preventive maintenance

Preventive maintenance is usually thought of as a way to ensure that facilities, production equipment and processes continue to run efficiently. Preventive maintenance also can help to ensure hazards do not develop. Scheduled preventive maintenance should be a part of every facility operating procedure, whether that process is operating the photocopy machine or producing a pesticide. Written preventive maintenance procedures should establish a schedule for the maintenance, identify the personnel responsible for the maintenance and describe a step-by-step process for keeping the equipment running safely. Preventive maintenance records should be kept and periodically reviewed to evaluate the effectiveness of the program. The records and procedures also should be reviewed during injury/illness/incident investigations to determine if adequate preventive maintenance might have helped to prevent the incident.

Element 4: Hazard recognition, evaluation and control review

Issues/questions	In place			Action plan (if "no" or "partially")
	Yes	No	Partially	
1. Is there a written, formal policy to control workplace hazards?				
2. Have written procedures been developed to be used in the hazard control program?				
3. Does the policy establish the participation of workers?				
4. Are there adequate resources for identifying and controlling hazards?				
5. Has an employee hazard reporting and follow-up system been developed?				
6. Has a hazard analysis procedure been established for identifying problem areas including: • Injury and illness records analysis? • Routine safety and health inspections? • A comprehensive baseline survey for safety and periodic, comprehensive update surveys? • Routine job hazard analysis? • A change analysis of planned and new facilities, processes, materials and equipment? • Employee reports of hazards? • Incident investigations? • Analysis of other records? • Trend analysis?				
7. Are hazards found in the worksite hazard analysis reviewed to determine what failure in the safety system permitted a hazard to occur?				
8. Has a risk assessment process been implemented?				
9. Does the process categorize risk presented by hazard according to: • Probability of occurrence? • Severity of outcome? • Employee exposure?				

Element 4: Hazard recognition, evaluation and control review

Issues/questions	In place			Action plan (if "no" or "partially")
	Yes	No	Partially	
10. Is the best practice approach of eliminating hazards during the design stage used?				
11. When hazard controls are required is the hierarchy of controls applied consistently?				
12. Are engineering controls always considered as the first and most reliable strategy to control hazards?				
13. Are personal protective equipment controls used as supplemental protection or as a last resort to control hazards?				

5

element

workplace design and engineering

Element 5: Workplace design and engineering

5.1 Management establishes a policy and procedures to ensure a design and start-up review process will be applied for all new or redesigned equipment and process systems. In implementing this policy, management will establish well-defined objectives, assess hazard probability and severity, establish design review procedures and use project checklists. The policy will establish minimum requirements and set responsibility and accountability when conducting design reviews. Design standards will be established for the following:

   5.1.1 Facility layout, workstation and machine design

   5.1.2 Relevant safety and health regulations and standards

   5.1.3 The relationship between the worker and the job (ergonomic design considerations)

   5.1.4 Proper material handling including both mechanical and manual handling

   5.1.5 The safety and health aspects of automated processes

   5.1.6 Life safety and fire protection

Overview

A safe and efficient work environment is achieved as a result of an ongoing process, including design and various stages of evaluation and modification. Designing "safety" into the workplace is as important as designing in efficiency. A workplace designed with safety and health considerations in mind will most likely enable employees to perform their tasks more efficiently, potentially resulting in higher productivity. Workplace features not designed with the safety and health of the employee in mind can cause employee fatigue, injuries or illness.

Safety and health professionals should be involved as consultants in the design stage, in start-up reviews and in evaluating equipment and materials proposed for purchase. Purchasing professionals must be aware of safety considerations, as well as United States and international standards, when making equipment purchases. Front-line employees also can make valuable contributions to the design process.

Safety and health hazards are most effectively and economically addressed in the planning and design stage through involvement of safety and health professionals and others in planning facilities, processes, materials and equipment. Safe workplace design reflects optimum physical and psychological compatibility between the employee and process, methods of operation, equipment, materials and machinery. Workplaces designed and constructed with employees in mind will have a favorable impact on productivity, quality, and safety and health.

Design and start-up review

Although design and start-up reviews are two distinct tasks, their purposes coincide. Both tasks focus on ways to identify and eliminate hazards and minimize harm should an injury, illness or incident occur. In general, both design and start-up reviews are conducted to identify and protect against chemical, physical, biological, mechanical, electrical, psychological and ergonomic hazards before the facility, process or equipment is used. The content of the reviews will depend on the industry, on whether the subject is a system or a piece of equipment and on the nature of the facility. Operations or tasks should be segregated into steps as a more manageable way to identify the hazards associated with each. This technique, called job safety analysis, is discussed in Element 7.

Design and start-up reviews should evaluate the effect of the following factors on the safety and health of the employees involved:

- Environment – chemical contaminants, heat/cold, humidity, lighting levels, noise, radiation
- Work flow – physical path, sequence, rate, duration
- Physical work layout and contents – size of space; type, size and location of instruments, controls and materials
- Work methods – physical and mental demands and information flow
- Guarding – physical means for preventing exposure to hazards

Element 5.1

Management establishes a policy and procedures to ensure a design and start-up review process will be applied for all new or redesigned equipment and process systems. In implementing this policy, management will establish well-defined objectives, assess hazard probability and severity, establish design review procedures and use project checklists. The policy will establish minimum requirements and set responsibility and accountability when conducting design reviews.

Review personnel should evaluate each factor in light of the best technical information available, and then make recommendations to alter the design or specification to eliminate or control the associated hazards so the risks are acceptable. Safety and health professionals coordinate input from other departments, such as purchasing and manufacturing, for example, to identify possible changes to eliminate or control hazards, as well as to identify which hazards cannot be eliminated. Hazards that cannot be eliminated through design are controlled through other means, such as placement and guarding of equipment to protect against exposure.

A design and start-up review procedure should be developed to provide operations, engineering and design personnel with direction and methods to foresee, evaluate and control hazards related to occupational safety and health when considering new or redesigned equipment and process systems. The procedure should define the scope of application, identify situations that are exempt from design review, establish roles and responsibilities for those who will participate in the review and initiate administrative procedures.

Element 5.1.1

Facility layout, workstation and machine design

Facility layout

Size, shape, location, construction and layout of buildings and facilities should permit the most efficient use of materials, processes and methods. Safety and health professionals should aim for efficient production with maximum employee safety. Four major factors should be considered in facility design:

1.   General design of the workplace
2.   Compliance with codes and standards
3.   Size, shape and type of buildings, processes and personnel facilities needed
4.   Life safety procedures and fire protection

Some principles to consider when planning internal facility layout include:
- Employees should recognize how materials, people and products flow through the facility.
- Employees should easily learn where things are located.
- Employees should move easily within, and to and from, the facility.
- Employees should be able to conveniently access services, such as the lunchroom and personnel office.
- Employees should be able to easily communicate with supervisors and access supervision offices.
- Employees should have a physical separation between noisy or hazardous areas.

Workstation design

When designing employee workstations, management should consider the following suggestions:
- Place controls where they require the least amount of movement.
- Provide lighting suitable to the task, as opposed to general illumination.

- Provide jigs and fixtures that relieve pressure.
- Provide a workbench so workers may either sit or stand as needed.
- Determine work flow patterns that are normal and easy for the worker.
- Provide use of audio and/or visual signals from machine operators.
- Pre-position materials, equipment, products and tools.
- Place tools, controls and materials in the employee's direct line of vision.
- Design the work flow so the work process moves smoothly.

Machine safeguarding

Machines with exposed moving parts can easily cause serious injury. Critical design features include those that prevent employees from coming into contact with the moving parts, eliminate or guard cutting edges and nip points and eliminate hot areas so injury can be avoided. Whenever possible, management should incorporate safeguarding into the design of machines. When a new piece of equipment is being considered or planned, the safety and health professional should evaluate the hazards posed by the machine. He or she should consider how the machine will be used, who will use it, how often it will be used and why. Using job safety analysis, the professional should evaluate each step in the machine's operation to identify all possible operator contacts with machine hazards.

There are numerous ways to safeguard machines. These safeguards will depend on the use of the machine and the possible hazard. Types of machine safeguards include:
- Physical barriers
- Electronic barriers
- Electrical interlocks
- Mechanical pull-back and sweep devices
- Guarding by location

Codes and standards

Facilities, processes and equipment should, at a minimum, meet all safety and health regulatory requirements. Many organizations also comply with voluntary standards established by public and private organizations. Such organizations include:
- Standards and specifications-setting organizations, such as the American National Standards Institute, the National Institute for Occupational Safety and Health, the International Organization for Standardization, which established the ISO 9000 series of manufacturing quality standards, the American Conference of Government Industrial Hygienists for chemical and physical agent exposures and the National Fire Protection Association
- Organizations such as Underwriters Laboratories and the National Institute for Occupational Safety and Health that publish lists of approved or tested devices

In the absence of applicable codes and standards, organizations should become aware of, and use, the best business practice for the industry.

Element 5.1.2
Relevant safety and health regulations and standards

Safety and health standards are subject to change, both in the United States and internationally. It is important to stay informed about current and proposed standards or addenda to standards. Many European countries require adherence to European Union directives, which address such workplace safety and health issues as material handling, video display terminals, personal protective equipment and equipment usage. The United Kingdom has regulations in place to address these directives.

Canada and Mexico have extensive legislation concerning safety and health. Companies should contact the safety and health office in the country or province of interest for the most current information. The best way to stay informed about standards, codes and best business practices is to subscribe to and read government publications (such as the *Federal Register* in the United States), as well as industry and safety and health publications.

Element 5.1.3

The relationship between the worker and the job (ergonomic design considerations)

Ergonomic factors

Ergonomics is the art and science of designing the work to fit the worker. Ergonomic reviews should be incorporated into any new facility design. An effective ergonomics program requires senior management commitment and continuing involvement to ensure the program remains an important feature of the organization's safety and health policy and to guarantee adequate resources to identify, evaluate, and control existing and potential ergonomic problems. The ergonomic program should:

- Encompass productivity, cost control, quality, maintainability, and safety and health considerations
- Identify existing and potential ergonomic problems
- Recommend corrective measures
- Implement improvements to enhance safety and health
- Monitor the effectiveness of the measures taken

Ergonomic design addresses employee- and task-related factors so the task can be performed efficiently and safely. The capability to perform a task may be affected by:

- An employee's physical condition, ability to judge, measure, reach, identify spatial relationships, withstand external exposures and adapt
- The tools used to perform the job
- The position the employee must assume to perform the task
- Location
- Strength requirements
- The amount of force that must be used to perform the job
- Weight of objects lifted
- Frequency of motion
- Stability of the workstation

A task involving repetitive reaching for an object on a low shelf requires the employee to continuously alternate between bending over and returning to an upright position. Eventually, the repetitive motion of bending and straightening can cause muscle fatigue and pain – signals of a mismatch between employee and task. Also, improper lifting techniques can impart sufficient stress on the back to cause a muscle strain or sprain. The situation calls for eliminating the need to bend by either moving the shelf, changing the placement of the object or altering the process needed to transfer the object.

Many injuries and illnesses related to hazards involving ergonomics become apparent only through time. Therefore, it is important to consider ergonomics in design review and job safety analysis as a means for preventing injuries and illness. Because hazards exist at the contact points between employee and task, the evaluation should focus on identifying the contacts and interactions between employees, equipment and processes. Then each contact point should be studied to identify the best way to accomplish the task efficiently and safely. Individuals involved in identification must be knowledgeable in research on human factors, engineering and biomechanics.

One way of identifying hazards is by analyzing data on work-related injuries and illnesses. Also, by analyzing near-injuries or pre-illness conditions, such as fatigue, companies can identify hazards related to ergonomics before they cause injuries or illness.

These hazards are often signaled by a host of physical ailments. Some examples include:
- Back pain
- Wrist, elbow and hand pain
- Neck and shoulder pain
- Blurred vision from eyestrain
- Muscle soreness

The causes of these problems can be investigated using incident investigation techniques; participation is usually required from qualified medical personnel.

Material handling

Within every business, there are material handling needs. Industrial operations, for example, must move raw material, component parts and finished products within the facility. Material handling is one of the most common tasks performed in an industrial setting.

Material handling accounts for 20 - 45 percent of all occupational injuries. If the materials are handled manually – without mechanical, hydraulic or other automated materials handling equipment – there are ergonomic hazards associated with lifting, carrying and placing.

Designers of systems and procedures should consider alternative ways for handling materials that will eliminate or minimize worker contact through, for example, automation or manually-controlled assists.

Procedures for handling all materials, whether manually or by automated means, must be reviewed to identify hazards. Examples of material handling hazards include:
- Sharp edges
- Acids or other toxic or hazardous substances packed in breakable containers
- Irritating dust
- Excessive load movement

Element 5.1.4

Proper material handling

- Load weight and stability
- Transport distance and elevation change
- Load manipulation

Ways to eliminate or control hazards should be defined, prioritized and implemented. Such controls include:
- Substituting materials
- Using handling aids
- Automating processes
- Decreasing load weight
- Providing additional training

Element 5.1.5

Safety and health aspects
of automated processes

Automated processes

Automated processes can save time, money and effort. While they minimize exposure to the hazards of the process, they also can create a new set of hazards to which employees can be exposed during operation, maintenance, equipment adjustments and sampling. These exposures must be addressed.

The nature of automated process hazards varies depending on the industry, the complexity and size of the systems. The safety and health professional, along with an engineer who understands robotics, must thoroughly evaluate the process identify all potential failure modes and contact points between humans and the process, and define all hazards. The design of the process should, if possible, eliminate hazards, minimize exposure to hazards and control the results of process failures. After the system is in place, and before it is online, the safety and health professional should evaluate the system again to identify any additional hazards undetected during design, construction and installation. These additional hazards should be addressed before the system is brought into operation.

Element 5.1.6

Life safety and fire protection

Life safety and fire protection

Adequate fire protection and life safety controls can minimize loss of life and property. Workplace design and construction are critical to fire protection and life safety. According to the National Fire Protection Association, fire protection measures should have the following general objectives:
- Saving lives
- Continuing operations
- Protecting property

Workplace design should address each of these objectives. To accomplish this, the designer must understand the uses and functions of the facility. Whether the facility is in the planning stage or already constructed, safety and health professionals should identify fire hazards and recommend ways to eliminate them or minimize the potential consequences of a fire or explosion. This process is called a fire hazard analysis. The issues considered in fire hazard analysis include:

- Site, including location, accessibility and age
- Construction materials and design
- Contents
- Operations
- Management of the facility
- People, including who is using the facility and how
- Fire protection system, including detection, alarms, communication, automatic sprinklers, portable fire extinguishers and fire brigades
- Emergency plans, procedures and evacuation

Effective fire protection measures consider the facility, the people in the facility and their actions, the potential for loss and the magnitude of existing hazards.

Additionally, specific fire codes – both construction and performance – must be followed at a minimum. A facility's design should include:

- Fire-resistant construction with fire divisions and self-closing fire doors
- Easy access to and exit from the facility interior
- A fire detection and alarm system
- An automatic sprinkler system
- Ready access to the facility to minimize emergency response time
- Adequate water supply
- Adequate portable fire extinguishers and other fire-fighting equipment
- Appropriate specialty equipment common to certain industries, such as blowout panels where explosions are possible and fixed non-water fire-suppression systems for valuable material storage areas, such as computer rooms, records storage and other important document repositories

Formal procedures for checking, testing and maintaining fire-protection equipment should be established and understood by employees assigned these responsibilities. The procedures identify responsible individuals and schedules and provide a means to monitor adherence. Procedures and equipment should be reviewed on an ongoing basis to identify needs and potential problems.

Element 5: Workplace design and engineering review

Issues/questions	In place			Action plan (if "no" or "partially")
	Yes	No	Partially	
1. Does management understand and adopt an "up-front" and "design in" approach to engineering and design?				
2. Does management communicate high priority for design-in safety?				
3. Does management place a high priority on process safety management for any automated processes?				
4. Does the organization have a policy to adhere to all relevant codes and standards, voluntary and statutory?				
5. Is a procedure in place for pre-design and pre-start-up reviews?				
6. Is adequate funding available for necessary analysis and reporting?				
7. Are those responsible for design trained in hazard identification and evaluation techniques?				
8. Are safety and health recommendations taken seriously and addressed in design?				
9. Are safety and health professionals involved in design and engineering decisions?				
10. Does management have a formal life safety policy, with saving lives as the primary objective?				
11. Are reviews conducted always? Sometimes? Occasionally? Never?				
12. Is the review procedure complete and adequate?				
13. Are ergonomic considerations regularly addressed in design and purchasing decisions?				
14. Are copies of all applicable codes and standards on site and reviewed?				

Element 5: Workplace design and engineering review

Issues/questions	In place			Action plan (if "no" or "partially")
	Yes	No	Partially	
15. Have facilities and processes been evaluated for adherence to codes and standards?				
16. Is a procedure in place for monitoring code adherence on a continuing basis?				
17. Does the safety and health department provide input into facility, work station and machine design specifications?				
18. Do procedures exist for fire safety analysis?				
19. Is fire safety analysis performed regularly?				
20. Are hazards involving material handling evaluation procedures in place?				

element 6

operational safety
and health programs

Element 6: Operational safety and health programs

6.1 Management establishes compliance policies for mandatory occupational safety programs based on regulations, as well as voluntary safety management system goals based on the needs of the organization. The regulatory compliance policy should:

    6.1.1 Set forth written procedures to be used in determining the applicability of government mandated standards.

    6.1.2 Direct staff to identify and implement best safety practices in applying a safety management system to the workplace.

    6.1.3 Ensure sufficient funds are budgeted for the implementation and ongoing needs of standards.

    6.1.4 Clearly define roles, responsibilities, expectations and accountability for compliance by all employees.

6.2 Management must determine the scope and nature of the organization's occupational health program and allocate resources to provide appropriate service. Management should develop program goals and establish functions, programs, procedures and activities to meet the organization's health goals. At a minimum, the health program should:

    6.2.1 Prevent occupational illnesses through control of risk factors.

    6.2.2 Ensure proper treatment of work-related illnesses and injuries.

6.3 Management must determine the scope and nature of the organization's occupational safety program and allocate resources to provide appropriate services. Management should develop program goals and establish functions, programs, procedures and activities to meet the organization's occupational safety goals. The two goals of an occupational safety program should be:

    6.3.1 To implement all safety programs required by mandatory standards

    6.3.2 To institute "best safety practices" and a proactive safety management system designed to prevent employee injuries

6.4 Management establishes policies and procedures for the effective management and control of external exposures. External exposures include any influences or risks that arise outside the boundaries of the company property or are caused by a third party. Five major types of external exposures include:

    6.4.1 Natural disasters

    6.4.2 Contract employees

    6.4.3 Vendors

    6.4.4 Products produced by the company

    6.4.5 Public liability

Overview

Some organizations consider the summation of the individual regulatory-based safety and health compliance programs as their "safety program." In a properly functioning safety management system, these individual operational safety and health programs can be a critical component in driving down employee injury rates. But without meaningful employee involvement in the design of such programs or consistent management commitment in requiring adherence to the requirements of such programs, the result of such efforts is a "paper program" that is written in a misguided attempt to show compliance with some regulatory standard. There is often little, if any, impact on employee injury rates.

Another common error is the failure of the organization to view safety in the context of a safety management system. When an organization understands it is working toward implementing a safety management system, it can assess its current state and then implement safety and health programs that close gaps in its current state and move it toward a more effective safety management system. Without a clear understanding of the safety management system to be implemented, organizations try one program after another, hoping this will drive down the injury rate. It rarely does.

It is critical that organizations understand that the occupational safety and health program is only one of the nine elements essential in a properly functioning safety management system that will effectively prevent employee injuries.

Occupational safety and health programs can be considered in terms of two broad types:

- The first type includes those programs imposed by regulatory agencies, such as the Occupational Safety and Health Administration or the Environmental Protection Agency.
- The second type includes additional programs required for compliance with voluntary programs such as OSHA's voluntary protection programs, international standards such as ISO's 18000, trade association requirements such as the American Chemical Industry's Responsible Care or internal safety management systems designed to prevent site specific occupational injuries or illnesses.

Failing to design and implement occupational safety and health programs that comply with regulatory standards can have a substantial impact on a company's public image and profits. In fact, OSHA inspections routinely result in fines totaling tens of thousands of dollars for noncompliance.

While the financial impact of such fines is easy to quantify, it is harder to calculate the damage done to a company's public image, it's standing in the community, or the organization's ability to attract and retain employees.

Companies with more progressive safety and health management systems correctly view regulatory standards as *minimal*. Such organizations often adopt "best safety practices" as a means to ensure the health and well being of employees. These "best safety practices" often require implementing safety and health management systems designed to prevent occupational illnesses and injuries by controlling and eliminating exposures to hazards even when no such regulatory standard exists.

Compliance with both regulatory and voluntary occupational safety and health programs is best achieved by a systematic approach that identifies which standards are to be implemented, an ongoing audit method to address issues of non-compliance, a method of assessment to determine program effectiveness in achieving organizational safety and health goals, and a method for monitoring future regulatory developments that may impact the organization.

This element focuses on four broad areas:
- Identification of mandatory standards and "best safety practices" required for an effective safety management system
- The role of occupational health programs in the prevention and care of occupational illnesses
- The role of occupational safety program in preventing employee injuries
- Control of external factors impacting the employees and the organization

Element 6.1

Management establishes compliance policies for mandatory occupational safety programs based on regulations, as well as voluntary safety management system goals based on the needs of the organization.

Compliance policies

There are a multitude of mandatory and voluntary safety and health programs that may impact an organization. There should be a specific policy identifying which individuals or groups are responsible for determining which mandatory standards must be implemented at the company and which voluntary standards would assist the organization in achieving its safety and health goals.

A formal mechanism to manage regulatory compliance issues should be in place to make sure existing and new regulations are adequately addressed.

Regulatory compliance management involves:
- Keeping informed about the changing United States and international laws and regulations
- Analyzing and applying appropriate regulations to the workplace
- Monitoring compliance through self-assessment techniques

Mandatory regulatory compliance should be viewed as a minimum, "broad brush" concept. These regulations are not specific or comprehensive enough to address the multitude of actual hazards present in the workplace. Therefore, the compliance program should be only one aspect of an organization's safety and health management system.

Mandatory standards

In the United States, federal, state and local governing bodies mandate some specific operational safety and health programs.

The primary federal safety and health law for business and industry is the

Occupational Safety and Health Act of 1970. The law (84 Statute 1593) was enacted to "assure ... every working man and woman in the Nation safe and healthful working conditions and to preserve our human resources," according to the preamble of the act.

The Occupational Safety and Health Administration establishes standards addressing both design issues – such as machine guarding and ventilation – and performance issues, including emergency planning, hazard communication and medical surveillance.

OSHA standards incorporate, by reference, previously established voluntary consensus standards developed by industry and government research and standard-setting organizations including:

- American Conference of Government Industrial Hygienists
- American National Standards Institute
- American Petroleum Institute
- American Society for Testing and Materials
- National Fire Protection Association
- National Institute for Occupational Safety and Health
- Underwriters Laboratories
- U.S. Department of Commerce
- U.S. Public Health Service

OSHA and the EPA

While the Occupational Safety and Health Act addresses the safety and health of a company's employees, several environmental laws address the safety and health of the surrounding community. These laws include the Resource Conservation and Recovery Act, the Comprehensive Environmental Response, Compensation and Liability Act (commonly known as Superfund), the Clean Air Act and the Superfund Amendments and Reauthorization Act, which includes emergency planning and community right-to-know provisions requiring Material Safety Data Sheets and other information related to the use and storage of hazardous substances is regularly transferred to local emergency response agencies.

Occupational and environmental safety and health laws are often closely interrelated, and coordination between the two sets of laws is crucial to ensure effective compliance. The EPA and OSHA have a memorandum of understanding addressing the interrelationship of occupational and environmental health and safety compliance schemes. This cooperation is designed to ensure standardization of compliance issues and prevention of redundancy and conflicting requirements.

Mine safety

The Mine Safety and Health Act of 1977 requires mine operators to comply with safety and health standards and sets forth numerous rights for mine workers, including specialized training. Standards under the act are included in 30 CFR 1-199. Proposed and new standards and regulations are published in the *Federal Register* and subject to public comment before they are finalized.

State and local programs

Section 18(H) of the Occupational Safety and Health Act allows states to establish, implement and enforce their own occupational safety and health plans as long as the plans are at least as effective as the federal program. State laws must include all issues and standards addressed by the federal program. Those standards not addressed in a state plan must then be enforced under the federal program. OSHA must approve all state plans, which must undergo a 3-year trial period to make sure they are effective. In states without state plans, the federal government enforces federal standards.

Local governments also may impose fire, electrical and building codes that impact safety and health.

International regulations and standards

The European Union comprises numerous European countries and was established to remove trade barriers within Europe and achieve a "single internal market." In 1989, the European Union adopted a framework for workplace safety and health standards. Called the Framework Directive, it establishes some general principles for workplace safety and health. "Daughter directives" have since been adopted by the European Union to set forth more specific regulatory requirements under the Framework Directive, including indoor air quality, video displays and personal protective equipment.

The intention of European Union safety and health regulations is to standardize safety and health requirements across Europe, so one unified standard may take the place of individual national standards. When possible, existing international standards are used to formulate directives. Member countries enact legislation to implement and enforce each directive.

There is no comprehensive national safety and health law in Canada. Safety and health laws and regulations are established and enforced by individual provinces. Funding for safety and health programs comes directly from employers. There is a substantial focus on employee participation and responsibility, and employees can be given the same penalties as employers for violating safety and health regulations.

Canadian inspectors have unlimited access to the workplace, and they have the authority to immediately shut down a work process that poses an imminent threat to the safety and health of employees.

In Mexico, the regulatory authority rests with the General Directorate of Medicine and Safety in the Workplace under the Mexican Secretary for Labor and Social Welfare. The federal government has enforcement responsibility for safety and health, with some assistance from state authorities. Like those in Canada, Mexican employees are liable for safety and health violations and can be fined.

Staying informed

Regulations are constantly being revised. New OSHA and other federal agency regulations are proposed frequently, while new directives and standards are being adopted by the

European Union. Achieving and maintaining compliance depends on continuously tracking regulations, analyzing their impact and responding. New, modified and proposed U.S. regulations are published in the *Federal Register*. For organizations in highly regulated industries, careful tracking of the *Federal Register* is an important routine and the best way to stay abreast of U.S. federal regulations. Many large companies employ full-time regulatory professionals to keep them informed of applicable new and proposed regulations. The regulations are sometimes difficult to understand and interpret, even for technically-trained professionals. And for a company dependent on staying in compliance, assigning a knowledgeable safety and health professional to track the *Federal Register* is a must.

The *Federal Register* and *Code of Federal Regulations* are readily available via the Internet and on CD-ROM. Computer versions of the regulations can be searched by word or topic, which simplifies the job of identifying pertinent regulations. Although these electronic documents are more expensive than the paper versions, organizations that must comply with numerous regulations may save considerable time and money by using these innovative tools.

Up-to-date information on international standards also is available through online computer networks. Subscribing to, and reading, safety and health professional journals also will help organizations stay informed about new regulatory developments in the United States, Canada, Mexico, Europe and elsewhere. The *Barbour Index* contains a reference source on legislation, standards, codes of practice and reports applicable to the United Kingdom. In addition, the U.S. Export Service can provide specific information on directives, standards and regulations affecting particular exports.

Individual states often provide free consulting services. Trade and professional associations specific to the company's industry usually keep track of relevant regulations and proposals. They offer technical information, low- or no-cost consulting services and advice.

Management should develop a protocol for staying informed on applicable regulations, delegating specific responsibility for tracking regulations and establishing a mechanism for communicating information to potentially affected departments about new, modified or proposed regulations. This task is commonly assigned to the organization's safety and health department.

Written policy

Management should implement a regulatory policy clearly stating what individuals or groups are responsible for determining which local, state, federal or international standards are applicable to the organization. The policy should be:

- In writing
- Establish a method of monitoring changes in regulations
- Provide assistance in effective implementation of mandatory operational safety and health programs
- Include an audit system to determine level of compliance
- Include an assessment system to determine effectiveness of existing programs in achieving the organization's safety and health goals

Element 6.1.1

Set forth written procedures to be used in determining the applicability of required standards.

Element 6.1.2
Direct staff to identify
and implement best management
practices in applying the safety
management system
to the workplace.

Best safety practices

Compliance with mandatory standards alone may not significantly impact an organization's injury and illness rate. Progressive organizations often will choose to comply with a "best safety practice" standard in an effort to drive down its injury rate. The advantage in adopting a specific "best safety practice," such as the implementation of an effective safety management system, is that the diverse resources of an organization can be called upon to achieve this goal.

OSHA offers its own version of best practices based on the belief that an effective safety and health management system is the best way to prevent occupational injuries and illnesses. Under the Voluntary Protection Program, OSHA considers participants that develop comprehensive site-specific management systems – examining management leadership, employee participation, consistent audits and continuing plans for improvement – as key elements.

ISO also developed the OHSAS 18000 series of standards including OHSAS 18001 Occupational Health and Safety Management Systems, developed in response to the success enjoyed by the ISO 9000 quality standards and ISO 14000 environmental standards. The American National Standard – Occupational Health and Safety Management Systems is expected to be the American equivalent of the OSHAS 18000.

Further, a growing number of trade groups and industry associations require or encourage members to develop safety management systems to prevent employee injuries and illnesses. As an example, consider the American Chemical Industry that incorporated its 106 responsible care management practices into a comprehensive responsible care management system.

Management should acknowledge that compliance with mandatory standards is inadequate to reduce employee injuries and illnesses, identify a safety management system as the most successful method to protect the well-being of the workers, and disseminate the safety management system throughout the organization so it is understood by all employees.

Element 6.1.3
Ensure sufficient funds are
budgeted for the implementation
and ongoing needs of standards.

Budgeting for safety

The distinct advantage of a regulatory policy identifying mandatory safety and health programs and "best safety practices" is the ability to budget for expenditures associated with program implementation and ongoing activities. It is easier to quantify costs and ensure they are included in budget allocations when activities are outlined for the coming fiscal year and are clearly understood.

Effective safety professionals understand organizations operate on a budget cycle. Budget allocations for the next fiscal year are often made several months prior to the start of the budget cycle. For example, if an organization's budget year parallels the calendar year it would begin January 1st and end December 31st. Depending on the size of the organization, budget allocations for the coming year may be allotted many months prior to the start of the fiscal year.

Practical safety professionals strive to ensure the safety costs associated with ongoing safety and health programs, as well as any new initiatives or projects, are considered in the budget planning.

Safety professionals should be prepared to justify the costs associated with safety and health programs. Expenditures may be justified through cost avoidance, lowered injury rates or reduced possibility of fines for non-compliance with regulations. Safety professionals should be prepared to justify costs associated with employee activities, such as joint safety committee meetings, through completed projects or numbers of hazards abated.

Additionally safety professionals should prepare to discuss costs associated with safety and health programs in terms of the organization's overall mission statement. If the company's mission statement indicates that a goal is to be the lowest cost producer, the safety professional should speak in terms of the need for healthy experienced employees to achieve that goal.

If the company mission states a goal is increased operating efficiencies, the safety professional needs to speak in terms of team efficiencies that are realized when healthy employees work together on a continuing basis or efficiencies realized when supervisors do not have to spend time looking for employees to replace injured or ill employees.

It is especially beneficial for the safety professional to discuss current and potential injury costs in terms of dollars as well as in terms of the amount of goods and services required to cover the direct costs of injuries. The cost of goods or services required to pay for the cost of injuries can be an eye opening experience for an organization.

The true cost of an injury: An example

An injury takes place resulting in direct costs for medical services and rehabilitation of $50,000. In this particular workplace, employees are producing a product that sells for $10 per unit, netting the company a 10 percent profit margin; for each $10 unit sold, the organization profits $1.

This company would have to produce, ship and sell 50,000 units to pay for the costs associated with that single $50,000 injury.

If the company produces 10,000 units per hour, five hours of production time would be dedicated to recouping the costs associated with this single injury.

If the company is self-insured, injury costs would come directly out of profits or add to losses. And if the company has workers' compensation insurance, injuries result in increased expenses through higher premiums. These higher expenses reduce profits.

Safety professionals can help their organizations understand that budget allocations for effective safety and health programs can increase profits by avoiding the direct and indirect costs associated with employee injuries and illnesses. Cost savings are in addition to enhanced public image, improved employee morale and fulfillment of basic corporate responsibility. When safety professionals justify their budget request and expenditures in terms of the broader impact on the organization, they tend to be viewed as dedicated to helping the organization achieve its goal, not as unwanted personnel imposed by a fear of regulatory agencies.

Roles and responsibilities

Element 6.1.4
Clearly define roles, responsibilities, expectations and accountability for compliance by all employees.

Effective safety professionals are able to describe their role and the roles of others in terms of specific responsibilities and specific behaviors. As an example, consider the OSHA general requirement for machine guarding (29 CFR 1910.212). In this example, it may be the specific responsibility of the site safety coordinator to initially inspect all new or altered processes for proper guarding. It may be the continuing responsibility of the area supervisor to verify that "equipment guards are in place" or that the correct "special hand tools" are being used by the employees. Too often, the supervisor is given no additional instructions.

In a properly functioning safety management system, the area supervisor in the above example would be able to list or show the exact machine guards for which he is responsible, would be able to describe what constitutes the guard in place or the guard missing, and list the exact "special hand tools" required by the process and describe their proper usage. Too often, supervisors or other employees are given compliance responsibilities in terms of vague generalities such as "make sure everything is guarded" or "make sure workers are using the right tools." Other examples of specific compliance instructions would include:

- Maintain a three-foot clearance in front of department-specific electric panels.
- Verify daily the three emergency exits in the department are lit and free of obstructions.
- Verify that any power tool being used in the department has the grounding prong in place.
- Verify that each department driver has conducted the required pre-inspection checklists.

Employees should be given clear specific instructions defining their responsibilities in implementing and maintaining compliance with mandatory and voluntary safety and health standards.

Occupational health

Element 6. 2
Management must determine the scope and nature of the organization's occupational health program and allocate resources to provide appropriate services. Management should develop program goals and establish functions, programs, procedures and activities to meet the organization's occupational health goals.

The occupational health program is an integral part of an organization's total safety and health effort. The two main goals of an occupational health program are to identify, evaluate and control exposure to risk factors that may lead to an occupational illness, and to assure proper treatment of work-related illnesses and injuries.

At a minimum, the program should address the immediate needs of injured or ill employees on the job through adequate first aid and response to emergencies. In the absence of a doctor's office, clinic or hospital near the workplace, employers must provide adequately trained and equipped personnel to render first aid to injured employees.

Management must determine the scope and nature of the company's occupational health program and allocate the resources to provide the appropriate services. The scope and nature of the program will depend on the size and nature of the organization's business, the types of activities performed and the available budget.

Management and safety and health professionals should develop program goals and establish functions, programs, procedures and activities to meet the company's occupational health goals. Management's continuing support will fuel the program's credibility and establish its authority.

The program should be monitored as it is implemented to identify areas for improvement. Particularly as a company grows and the face of its workforce changes, its needs for occupational health services also will change.

Although the primary focus of most occupational health programs is on the health and well being of employees on the job, occupational health also is affected by the employees' lives away from work. Injuries and illness resulting from off-the-job activities and lifestyles may diminish a person's health to the point where occupational demands can more easily cause or exacerbate an existing health condition. A fully successful occupational health program promotes the health and well being of employees both on and off the job. Off-hours health issues can be addressed through physical conditioning and wellness programs, screening for common health problems, such as increased cholesterol and high blood pressure, and educational materials on such topics as healthy lifestyles.

Every company has different occupational health needs, depending on the nature of operations and the hazards they present. The company occupational health program should address maintenance of employee medical and exposure records, employee health services, employee disabilities and rehabilitation, worksite exposure monitoring, periodic medical examinations and medical surveillance as appropriate to the activities and operations taking place at the facility.

Occupational health professionals

Specialized health professionals, including occupational health physicians, occupational health nurses, industrial hygienists and health physicists, may provide occupational health services.

Occupational physicians are medical doctors with specialized training in work-related diseases, illnesses and injuries. Depending on the hazards and nature of operations and the size and complexity of the occupational health program, a company may need the services of a full-time, part-time or consulting physician. Many companies contract physicians' services through local occupational medicine clinics. Clinics also may provide placement and other more specialized physical examinations, treatment of injuries and other consulting services.

Organizations should strive to develop continuing relationships with occupational physicians. One of the goals of the relationship would be to have the doctor reasonably familiar with the nature of the processes, job demands of the employees and risk factors to which an employee has been exposed. Physicians who are familiar with employee worksites often are more effective in diagnosing and treating employee injury and illnesses and rehabilitating employees.

Occupational health nurses have specialized training in work-related illnesses and injuries. Occupational health nurses work with occupational health physicians to develop and maintain a company's occupational health program. In addition to treating routine occupational illnesses and injuries under the direction of the occupational health physician, occupational health nurses often are responsible for filing workers' compensation claims, maintaining employee medical records and educating employees on work and non-work-related health issues. Although occupational health nurses can provide many health services, they cannot take the place of a physician in diagnosing and treating serious work-related illnesses and injuries.

Industrial hygienists

Industrial hygienists are trained to anticipate, identify and evaluate physical, chemical and biological health hazards in the workplace and recommend control procedures for these hazards. They maintain their skills through continuing study and professional certification. Some hygienists have training in specialized disciplines such as epidemiology, toxicology, acoustics or ventilation systems. Industrial hygienists use sensitive instruments to measure exposure levels. Depending on need, an organization may use in-house industrial hygienists or contract with outside hygienists available through insurance companies or private consulting firms.

After identifying a hazard, the industrial hygienist evaluates the degree of exposure and severity of impact on employees. After evaluating the hazard, the industrial hygienist recommends a means for controlling exposure or eliminating the hazard.

Ergonomists are specialists who evaluate the interface of the worker and the environment with the primary focus of preventing musculoskeletal disorders. Ergonomics is the scientific discipline concerned with interactions among humans and other elements of a system – such as tools, equipment, products, tasks, organization, technology and environment. The profession applies theory, principles, data, methods and analysis to design in order to optimize human well being and overall system performance.

Health physics is a discipline dedicated to protecting humans and the environment from radiation hazards. Health physicists are employed by organizations to identify, evaluate and address radiation hazards in the workplace. Radioactive materials are used in many occupational settings, including:
- Hospitals and medical clinics
- Utilities
- Industrial radiography operations
- Manufacturing facilities that use X-rays as part of quality control operations
- Biomedical research facilities

Organizations that use radioactive materials should have an effective radiation safety program. A radiation safety officer should be appointed to oversee the program, provide education to employees exposed to radioactive materials and assure compliance with monitoring, record keeping and exposure control programs.

Preventing occupational illness

Most work places will have at least some risk factors that may lead to an occupational illness. As an example, consider an office worker exposed to the ergonomic risk factors of repetition and awkward postures who may develop carpal tunnel syndrome. Employees in construction, general industry, mining, service, agriculture and maritime industries are routinely exposed to a number of risk factors for occupational illnesses.

The presence of risk factors does not necessarily mean any worker will develop an occupational illness. But the goals of an occupational health program should be to ensure:

- Risk factors in the worker's environment that may cause an occupational illness are clearly identified.
- Employees are trained to recognize signs and symptoms that may indicate an overexposure to a risk factor and the potential onset of an occupational illness.
- That risk factors are evaluated to determine the probability of uncontrolled exposure resulting in an occupational illness
- That engineering controls, administrative controls and personal protective equipment are capable of reducing employee exposure to the risk factor to a level of acceptable risk

Risk factors

Four broad categories of risk factors that may result in occupational illnesses are risks, factors related to chemical, biological, ergonomic and physical hazards.

If a goal of an occupational health program is to prevent worker illness, evaluation of chemical exposures must occur. The four main routes of chemical entry to the body are inhalation (breathing in a chemical), ingestion (eating), absorption through the skin and injection.

An occupational health program should be able to readily identify those chemicals in the workplace that are capable of resulting in chronic illnesses, such as silicosis, cancer, asthma or sensitization, as well as acute illness such as respiratory tract irritations or dermatitis.

In addition to chemical exposures, an occupational health program should consider the biological risk factors that may cause occupational illnesses. Every workplace should consider that the HIV virus might be present among its workforce. Additional biological agents such as hepatitis and turburculosis may be planned for by occupational physicians.

Other biological risk factors include exposure to animal wastes, such as bird droppings or rat droppings, and exposure to mold or exposure to bacteria, such as the legionella bacteria that may be present in cooling towers or water mists.

Element 6.2.1

Prevent occupational illnesses through control of risk factors

Ergonomic risk factors in a workplace capable of causing musculoskeletal disorders include repetition, awkward postures, forceful exertions and even environmental factors such as glare and temperature extremes. Physical factors in the workplace that may lead to occupational illnesses include noise that results in hearing loss, temperature extremes leading to heat exhaustion or hypothermia, and infrared or ultraviolet light from welding and other operations that may result in eye disorders.

Monitoring the workplace for exposures to risk factors capable of causing occupational illnesses is an integral part of a company's occupational health program.

Several types of worksite monitoring can be conducted as part of the occupational health program. These include personal exposure monitoring, work area monitoring, biological monitoring and medical monitoring. Additional forms of monitoring include job safety observations, employee interviews and worksite surveys. Personal exposure and work area monitoring may be conducted by industrial hygienists to evaluate the levels of potentially harmful agents in the workplace and determine the need for controls.

Biological monitoring requires evaluating bodily fluids or tissues for the presence of harmful agents. A physician equipped with a specialized laboratory to measure even extremely low levels of substances, including radioactive contaminants, in human tissue, usually performs biological monitoring. Because some types of biological monitoring involve invasive procedures, it is used mainly when exposure potential and the hazard are severe enough to warrant such measures. Medical personnel conduct medical monitoring to evaluate the physical and psychological effects of potentially harmful agents. Medical monitoring may include taking medical and work histories, physical examinations, X-rays and laboratory tests and testing hearing and vision. Monitoring records are helpful for identifying exposures to health hazards before they cause serious illness or injury to employees.

Another form of worksite evaluation is ongoing medical examinations targeted at evaluating exposure to specific occupational illness risk factors. This medical evaluation program is commonly referred to as medical surveillance.

Medical surveillance is used particularly when employees may have been exposed to certain chemicals or other harmful agents such as lead, cadmium or noise in the workplace. At the pre-placement physical examination, audiometric baselines or baseline levels of the relevant substances can be measured, often in blood or urine. Changes in hearing through time are measured in subsequent audiograms. Changes in biological levels of metals are periodically remeasured and compared to established standards to make sure the exposure stays below the standard. Increased levels or those approaching or exceeding the standards may indicate a serious health hazard.

The frequency and scope of medical surveillance will depend on the type of hazards to which employees are exposed and are often regulated by governmental agencies. In some cases, medical examinations might be provided for employees as a service - on a voluntary, annual basis, for example. In other cases, where exposure to specific hazardous agents is possible, regulations may require medical examinations at specified frequencies.

The nature of the needed exam may vary, from drawing and analyzing blood for a targeted agent to taking X-rays and conducting comprehensive examinations.

The occupational health program should define and specify in writing the conditions and criteria for medical surveillance. Guidelines for conducting and maintaining medical surveillance records have been published by regulatory agencies and other organizations.

Employees involved with worksite analysis and worksite monitoring should be made familiar with signs and symptoms that may indicate an overexposure to an illness risk factor or the early onset of the disease. If these early symptoms should appear, employees may be sent for medical intervention.

Hierarchy of controls

As in any safety issue, engineering controls should always be the primary method used to control exposure to risk factors for occupational illnesses. Administrative controls, such as job rotation, may limit the duration of exposure to a risk factor, but may ultimately increase the total number of employees exposed. Use of personal protective equipment, such as respirators or earplugs, are often the least effective means of preventing occupational illnesses. Personal protective equipment only serves as a barrier between the risk factor and the employee. Protection depends largely on the personal protective equipment being properly fitted and used.

Safety professionals can be instrumental in helping organizations move toward engineering controls as the main method of addressing risk factors for occupational illnesses.

One of the best methods is to calculate the cost of ongoing compliance programs with the cost of an engineering control. The initial outlay for a dust collection device, for example, may seem high until compared with the costs associated with an ongoing respiratory program. Similarly, it may be less expensive to isolate or replace a source of noise than pay for audiometric testing, hearing protection and cost of training required by a hearing conservation program.

Safety professionals can again discuss the engineering expenditures in terms of not only protecting the employees from illnesses but also as being more cost effective.

A final note on engineering controls: There should be an expectation that engineering controls will be used whenever such controls are installed in the workplace. Engineering controls, like ergonomic lift equipment, are a waste of company resources if the equipment is left idle after training is completed. It is normally the responsibility of the safety professional to define the specific behaviors expected in using the engineering controls. It may be the responsibility of the safety professional to see that employees are able to demonstrate mastery of those behaviors after training is completed. It is normally the responsibility of the line supervisors and managers to see that the engineering controls are routinely and properly used.

Health promotion programs

Obesity, cardiac disease, cancer and a variety of other illnesses can impact the workforce of any organization. Illnesses that do not originate in the workplace can still have a substantial impact on an organization's overall competitiveness through loss of personnel and increased insurance cost. Some organizations attempt to protect their employees through worksite health promotion programs.

Worksite health promotion programs educate employees on living a healthy lifestyle both on and off the job. The emphasis in these "wellness" programs is on preventing disease. The payoff to the organization is a better informed and healthier workforce, resulting in increased productivity, decreased absenteeism, lower turnover and potentially lower workers' compensation costs, plus possible decreases in medical insurance claims.

The health promotion program may focus on one issue, such as stress or hypertension, or may be a comprehensive program incorporating numerous aspects of physical and psychological well being. The program may include informational materials, classes, workshops or counseling. Some companies provide exercise equipment or membership in a local health club as part of their health promotion program. Smaller organizations can create a health promotion program by coordinating or pooling resources with other companies. Also, companies often can use community resources to provide health promotion programming. Fire departments and hospitals often can provide a combination of on-site and off-site services to educate and work with employees on wellness issues.

Element 6.2.2

Ensure proper treatment of work-related illnesses and injuries.

Treatment

A life-threatening illness, such as a heart attack, or life-threatening injury, such as an amputation with severe bleeding, can occur without warning. In such an event, critical care must be available within minutes. An organization must consider carefully if a call to an outside emergency responder or a 911 call will be able to have trained personnel responding to the life-threatening event within the recommended 3 - 6 minutes.

If it is not realistic to expect outside responders to assist a severely stricken employee within minutes, alternate arrangements must be made.

First aid is the immediate care given to an injured or suddenly ill person. It consists of providing temporary care until proper medical treatment, if needed, is given.

All injured or suddenly ill employees should receive first-aid treatment, no matter how minor or serious the injury or illness. All injuries and illnesses must be reported. Prompt reporting and treatment of injuries and sudden illnesses is important to make sure proper attention is given to the victim and to ensure accurate workers' compensation reporting and OSHA record keeping. Companies also can use the recorded information to help correct the cause of the injury in order to prevent recurrences. Because first-aid requirements vary outside the United States, companies should check with the country's Labor Ministry or Department for current requirements.

How many should be trained?

Many organizations have adopted a goal of having 10 percent of their workforce trained in first aid. Consider a three-shift operation with 480 employees. The goal of training 48 employees can be easily accomplished by training one fourth of the goal each quarter. This organization would train 12 employees in first aid every three months. The advantage to this method is two-fold. First it is relatively easy to train 12 responders in a single day-long class. And second, the spacing of the training during a period of a year results in at least some percentage of the employees being trained within three months of any injuries or illnesses that may occur.

The first-aid kit and supplies should be inspected regularly on a scheduled basis to make sure the supplies are replenished as needed and to replace all expired, out-of-date or nonworking supplies. Access to first-aid supplies should be restricted to the first-aid practitioner. No ingestible medications should be given to employees except under the supervision of a nurse or physician.

First-aid supplies and a trained first-aid provider are required when timely medical treatment is not otherwise available. In addition, all designated first-aid providers should be trained and maintain first-aid certification under a program approved by the appropriate government agencies and provided by an established organization, such as the National Safety Council.

Employee health services

On-site health services should be located in a dedicated area within the facility. The health service location should be private and clean, with adequate space to treat multiple cases at the same time and allow privacy for male and female patients. The health service space should have hot and cold running water and toilet facilities and should be adequately ventilated. Ideally, the clinical area should consist of a waiting room, a treatment room and a consultation room. Larger facilities also may have rehabilitation areas, dressing areas or conference rooms, and facilities for taking X-rays and performing laboratory tests and rehabilitation.

Medical examinations

Medical examinations are needed for a variety of reasons, including the following:
- *Pre-placement.* Pre-placement examinations or pre-placement evaluations are routinely made before hiring a new employee or transferring a current employee to another job. A medical exam establishes a new employee's medical condition and compares the physical condition of the employee with the documented requirements of the job. If pre-placement physicals are performed on acceptable candidates for a particular position, they must be performed on all applicants and employees being considered for that position. The examination reveals whether the

101

employee is medically qualified to perform the stated job tasks and whether the job is medically suitable for the employee. When the job and the condition of the employee are determined to be medically incompatible, the physician or other occupational health professional should recommend ways to modify the job tasks or equipment to accommodate the employee, which would be in accordance with the Americans with Disabilities Act. The physician should then perform periodic follow-up examinations to ensure the job and the worker continue to be compatible. Information obtained in the examination must remain confidential.

- *Return to work after an illness or injury.* A physical examination is often conducted when an employee returns to work after a prolonged illness. The objective is to determine whether the employee is able to perform all the required work activities immediately or whether work restrictions are applicable, which can allow for activities to be phased in gradually. The supervisor and the physician can work as a team with the employee to identify any modifications needed.

- *Exit examination.* Exit examinations record the medical and health condition of the employee upon leaving employment. They provide feedback to the organization on the impact of job tasks on the medical condition of employees. By officially recording the medical condition of employees when they leave the company, exit examinations can provide medical documentation in case of any future legal claims.

Employees with disabilities

Employees with disabilities often can handle many job functions, depending upon their limitations. The occupational health team should work with these employees and other organized resources to find the safest and most effective approaches to performing the work tasks. Although the human resources department usually has the primary responsibility for placing and working with employees with disabilities, the occupational health physician and/or nurse should evaluate the employee to define limitations and work restrictions and then, in collaboration with other safety and health and related professionals, recommend ways to address or overcome the identified barriers where accommodations can be made.

Medical records

United States regulations require employers to maintain records that include employee exposures to toxic materials, radiation and high noise levels. The nature and extent of medical record-keeping requirements outside the United States vary; companies should contact the country's Labor Ministry or Department for current requirements.

Medical records can be analyzed to set health standards, place employees in jobs consistent with any physical or other limitations, provide support documentation for insurance claims and make accurate diagnoses of illnesses. They also can be used to help monitor the effectiveness of the company's safety and health management system and justify improvements in existing programs. Although medical records are useful in many ways to help evaluate and improve practices, procedures and conditions in the workplace, access to records must be strictly limited to health personnel and individual, personal confidentiality maintained.

Medical records can include the employee's medical history, the results of physical examinations and tests, descriptions of injuries and illnesses and records of exposure to harmful or toxic agents. Exposure records report the history of the employee's exposure to the agent, describe the work conditions that may have resulted in the exposure and any other related information and contain relevant data from the Material Safety Data Sheets. Depending on the nature of the exposure and the industry, medical and exposure records may need to be kept for up to 30 years past termination of a person's employment.

The medical record retention program should be established formally in writing. Companies must formally delegate and monitor authority and responsibility for keeping those records. The occupational health nurse or other health provider should maintain medical records, which should be considered an important professional responsibility. Sometimes, particularly when there are no full-time dedicated health professionals, medical records are kept by the personnel officer or equivalent. Medical records on individual employees must be kept in a location that is separate from other personnel records.

Procedures for recording, reporting, maintaining and retrieving records should be implemented and their effectiveness monitored. Storage locations for records, access procedures and confidentiality must all be addressed.

Management should direct and focus the priorities of the occupational health program. The occupational health program is an integral part of an organization's total safety management system. The scope and nature of the program will depend on such considerations as legal requirements, how the organization views its responsibilities, its perception of sound business practices and its financial resources.

Occupational safety programs

While occupational health programs focus on the prevention of occupational illnesses, occupational safety programs focus on the prevention of occupational injuries. Injuries are usually instantaneous events. Examples would be broken bones, lacerations and chemical burns. Professional assistance is available from occupational safety professionals and practitioners.

Certified Safety Professional is a safety professional who has met education and experience standards, has demonstrated by examination the knowledge that applies to professional safety practice, continues to meet the Continuance of Certification requirements established by the Board of Certified Safety Professionals and is authorized by the board to use the Certified Safety Professional (CSP) designation.

Professional engineers have fulfilled the education and experience requirements and passed the rigorous exams that, under state licensure laws, permit them to offer engineering services directly to the public. Professional engineers take legal responsibility for their engineering designs and are bound by a code of ethics to protect the public health and safety.

Element 6.3

Management must determine the scope and nature of the organization's occupational safety program and allocate resources to provide appropriate services. Management should develop program goals and establish functions, programs, procedures, and activities to meet the organization's occupational safety goals.

Engineering licensure laws vary by state; however, in general, an individual must be a graduate of an engineering program accredited by the Accreditation Board for Engineering and Technology, pass the Fundamentals of Engineering exam, gain four years of experience working under a professional engineer, and pass the Principles and Practice of Engineering exam to become a professional engineer.

Other safety professionals hold Advanced Safety Certificates from the National Safety Council and have attended at least three week-long classes in occupational safety and health. Students will have successfully completed the requirements of classes in Principles of Occupational Safety and Health, as well as in two of the following classes Safety Training Methods, Safety Management Techniques and Fundamentals of Industrial Hygiene. This broad view of the safety profession allows students to effectively function as a site safety person.

Element 6.3.1

Implement all safety programs required by mandatory standards

Mandatory standards

Occupational safety programs are a critical component of a properly functioning safety management system. One of the goals of the system should be to implement all safety programs required by mandatory standards.

Because of the number of federal, state, and local standards, it is not possible to write a single list addressing all situations, in all industries. The nine examples listed below are broadly based on the federal OSHA standards for general industry.

- **Establish emergency response procedures.** Every employee should be trained in the specific actions to take in various emergencies. At a minimum, employees should understand their roles in the event of fire, weather or natural disaster, such as a tornado or earthquake, release of a hazardous substance, medical emergency, the presence of an intruder, workplace violence or terrorist action. Within the scope of emergency planning are a number of safety or compliance issues that must be addressed.

  - Programs must be established to maintain emergency response equipment such as fire extinguishing systems, alarms, escape routes and first-aid supplies.
  - Even in the absence of an emergency response team, an emergency response plan must be developed designating a chain of command and other responsibilities during the alarm and evacuation phases.
  - Procedures must be developed to respond to a chemical spill or other release of a hazardous substance.
  - Procedures must be developed if rescue should become necessary during confined space entry.
  - Coordinate emergency response expectations with outside responders. There should be a clear agreement on roles and capabilities prior to an emergency call.

- **Establish housekeeping standards.** Poor housekeeping is often a contributing factor in employee injuries. Poor housekeeping also contributes to loss of profits through material loss, time wasted in looking for materials and tools and a general lowering of employee morale. It is the responsibility of management to define how an area or line should be maintained. This means a standard defining what is a "clean" area or line, adequate storage methods are provided, that frequency of cleaning is specified, and that employees are trained on the housekeeping standard.

- **Establish inspection protocol in the event of a regulatory agency inspection.**
  - Establish a compliance file that holds all documents that may be required to show compliance with a standard. Examples of such documents would include the OSHA 300 logs, the hazard communication plan, the personal protective equipment hazard assessment, noise monitoring records and training records.
  - Identify and train individuals who will be participating in regulatory inspections on proper protocol. Procedures should be developed for the arrival of an inspector, individuals who will participate in the opening conference and location of that opening conference should be identified, individuals who will participate in any inspection tours, and procedures should be developed for the closing conference and responding to any compliance findings. It is generally in an organization's best interest to resolve as many compliance findings as possible before the inspection is concluded.

- **Establish personal protective equipment procedures.**
  - Conduct and certify a site-specific personal protective equipment hazard assessment. The certification statement should be maintained with the inspection documentation.
  - Document types of engineering controls considered and rejected in favor of personal protective equipment.
  - Obtain and distribute required personal protective equipment setting up equipment maintenance procedures.
  - Train impacted employees.
  - Develop procedures to monitor ongoing effectiveness of the personal protective equipment in use.

- **Establish hazardous material storage and usage procedures.**
  - Establish procedures identifying maximum quantities to be stored onsite and storage procedures for hazardous substance.
  - Establish a hazard communication system that includes proper labeling, communication of hazards through Material Safety Data Sheets, and training of employees on routine usage and under emergency releases.
  - Establish spill control procedures.
  - Establish protocol for mandatory federal and state environment reporting, such as hazardous waste procedures and emergency response and community right-to-know reports.

- **Establish safe operating procedures.**
  - Establish machine safe-guarding requirements.
  - Establish electrical safe-guarding requirements.
  - Establish procedures for the use of power tools.
  - Establish procedures for welding and cutting.
  - Establish a hot work permit system.
  - Establish a confined space entry system.
  - Establish a fall protection program.
  - Establish a permit system for opening pipelines and attached equipment.

- **Establish material handling procedures.**
  - Establish procedures for power motor vehicles such as forklifts. Procedures should include operator training and equipment inspection procedures.
  - Establish procedures for cranes and other mechanical material handling .
  - Establish shipping/receiving procedures.

- **Establish incident investigation procedures.**
  - Establish procedures for the reporting of injuries and illnesses. Employees conducting incident investigations should be trained on root cause analysis.
  - Establish procedures for near miss reporting. Near misses are a warning sign that there is something occurring in the workplace that may result in an injury.
  - Establish procedures for maintaining OSHA 300 logs, first notice of injury and workers' compensation forms.

- **Establish hazardous energy control procedures.**
  - Establish electrical safety procedures including training for qualified and non-qualified procedures.
  - Establish a lockout-tagout procedure for the control of hazardous energy.
  - Establish a procedure for maintaining proper clearances around electric equipment including labeling of all equipment switches.

Element 6.3.2

Institute "best safety practices" and proactive programs designed to prevent employee injuries.

Proactive safety programs

Regulatory-based safety programs alone are inadequate to ensure excellence in safety management systems. Management also should institute "best safety practices" and proactive programs designed to prevent employee injuries.

In general, proactive safety initiatives are:

- Activities designed to abate hazardous conditions such as pre-start-up safety reviews, safety inspections, safety training and safety meetings
- Activities designed to encourage safe behaviors, such as job hazard analysis and job safety observations
- Incentive programs based on employees participating in proactive programs, such as joint safety committees

Controlling external exposures

Without an awareness of potential liability from external exposures, coupled with a comprehensive plan to identify and minimize exposure in those areas in which problems can arise, a company is at risk – not only for incidents, injuries and illnesses but also for substantial financial loss.

If external exposures are not well managed and controlled, they can cost a company time and money. They can result in loss of business and reputation. And, they can have political repercussions at the local, state and even federal level.

External exposures include any influence on risk arising outside the boundaries of company property or caused by a third party. Common types of external exposures result from actions connected with:

- Disasters caused by severe weather or natural events, hazardous substance releases originating from external sources, intruders or workplace violence and terrorist actions
- Onsite contractors
- Vendors
- Products produced by the company
- Public liability

Effective programs for managing and controlling external exposures need to incorporate key characteristics. For example, senior management must be strongly committed to and demonstrate highly visible leadership in the company's comprehensive safety and health program. In addition, underlying administrative or procedural systems must be in place and operational. Management must assign specific responsibilities to individuals to develop appropriate control systems for external hazards and hold individuals accountable for system functions. At a minimum, such programs should include the following components:

- Assessment of external exposure to risk including possible terrorist threats to region
- Development of appropriate compliance procedures, such as emergency response plans and contractor safety programs
- Monitoring of changes in legislation, regulations and licensing; tracking of phase-in and compliance dates and modifying of safety programs accordingly
- Measurement of performance by performance-based criteria, such as employee performance during emergency drills, number of contractor behaviors that are safe or at risk and ability to respond to product recalls
- Timely reporting of significant matters so they can be closely monitored by management

Natural disasters

The National Safety Council recommends emergency planners consider, at a minimum, six elements – medical emergencies, fire, hazardous material release, natural disasters, workplace violence or intruders and terrorist acts.

Element 6.4

Management establishes policies and procedures for the effective management and control of external exposures. External exposures include any influences or risks that arise outside the boundaries of the company property or are caused by a third party.

Element 6.4.1

Natural disasters

107

Emergency response planning for natural disasters requires a careful assessment of the locations in which the organization functions. The probability of hurricanes, tornadoes, earthquakes, flash flooding, blizzards and other natural disasters must be included in emergency response plans.

Releases of hazardous substances from external sources may require an evacuation. Such a release also may require employees be sheltered in place until the chemical plume has dissipated. Emergency response planning must consider the capacity to shelter employees from either hazardous substance releases or weather-related emergencies.

Regulatory considerations, including those pertaining to the environment, also must be taken into account in emergency response planning. If there is a possibility of environmental damage to nearby communities, operations need to meet emergency requirements of regulatory agencies.

Government, industry and the community need to work together to develop comprehensive emergency action plans. Companies should provide detailed information about their hazardous materials to local emergency planning committees to use in developing emergency response plans for the communities. The committees also are responsible for making the information available to the public.

In addition, companies that have and use toxic chemicals are required to report any emissions of these materials into the air, land and water. If a hazardous chemical is released, companies must notify local, state and federal officials immediately, as well as the local emergency planning committee. Written reports about the incident need to be available to the community.

Management should have a trained and experienced person review and monitor applicable regulations and standards. Within the United States, such standards include:
- Comprehensive Environmental Response Compensation and Liability Act
- Superfund Amendments and Reauthorization Act
- OSHA's Hazardous Waste Operations and Emergency Response
- OSHA's Hazardous Communication Standard
- Clean Air Act
- Clean Water Act
- Resource Conservation and Recovery Act
- Toxic Substances Control Act
- Federal Insecticide, Fungicide and Rodenticide Act
- Comprehensive Environmental Response Compensation and Liability Act
- Hazardous Materials Transportation Uniform Safety Act
- Pollution Prevention Act of 1990

Workplace violence as well as the presence of any unauthorized personnel should be considered in emergency response planning. It is often helpful to assess how difficult or easy it is for an individual to gain access to the worksite. Terrorist threats may require industry specific actions. All employers should consider planning information available from the Department of Homeland Security.

Contract employees

Organizations that bring outside workers onsite or contract for the services of workers employed by an outside firm need effective contractor control programs to reduce exposure to potential losses. Such programs must be carefully developed and managed. Two basic issues must be addressed: the onsite hazards of which contractors should be aware and hazards being created by the work for which the contractor was hired.

Host employers need to establish guidelines affording contractors' workers at least the same quality of safety and health protection afforded the employer's own workforce.

Depending upon the terms of the contract, employers and contractors often are responsible for the safety of their own personnel. However, despite contract language, host employers will not be able to avoid liability if incidents or injuries occur. Many regulatory agencies hold the host employer in charge – implying the host employer bears the ultimate responsibility for safety. An effective contractor control program provides oversight functions with respect to contractors.

Preplanning is one of the program's most important elements. As part of preplanning, the host employer should designate a coordinator to be responsible for contracted activities. A company needs to protect its interests by assigning safety and health responsibilities to a trained, experienced individual.

It is important that contractor orientation programs consider the need of all contract employees, not just skilled tradesman like electricians or masons. Contract employees who provide janitorial services are employed seasonally or for short term projects, or other temporary contract workers still need to understand the host site's rules and procedures. It is especially true that these employees need to understand the emergency alarms and response system.

Assuring contractor safety

As a first step in preplanning specific projects, the host employer must assess hazards and exposures. Is fatality a real possibility if safety procedures are not followed? Does the project for which the contractor is being hired require special training – for example, in confined spaces? Or, is the potential for hazard and exposure less because of the nature of the project? For instance, does the project require welding around exposed gas lines or merely painting a fence?

For all contract employees, the host employer needs to establish minimum guidelines for safety and health issues, making sure all regulatory requirements – such as obtaining necessary permits – have been addressed by contractors.

To minimize risk, use specific safety performance criteria for selecting contractors. Companies contracting for outside services need to make sure the contractors they use have written safety and health programs and good safety records. Many companies pre-qualify contractors, requiring them to submit information on their past safety performance. This data is reviewed, and only companies with acceptable safety records are invited to submit proposals. Before the bidding process begins,

Element 6.4.2

Contract employees

109

contractors should provide the following information for the preceding three years:
- Contractor safety and health procedures
- Contractor specialized training, if necessary
- OSHA 300 logs
- Experience modification ratios (workers' compensation loss versus premium history)

Employers should check contractors' experience modification rate. An experience modification rate of one is considered average, less than one is better than average and more than one is worse than average. To reduce your risk as the host employer, consider limiting contractors under consideration to those who have an experience modification rate equal to or less than one. If a contractor's experience modification rate is more than one, explore efforts during the past 18 months taken to improve the program. The contractor may have implemented a safety program but the experience modification rate has yet to be affected.

As part of the pre-qualification process, ask contractors to submit documents indicating their commitment to safety. These documents can be specified in the request for proposal. For instance, a host employer may request a contractor's written safety program. Additionally, the host employer may ask for a copy of the contractor's safety orientation program, workers' compensation management program and the contractor's enforcement and disciplinary procedures for safety violations.

Contractors may be asked how they would budget for safety equipment for the project or to describe their program for compliance with applicable regulatory requirements. For example, will personal protective equipment be required? If so, what will be supplied? Are training and maintenance procedures for contractor-supplied equipment adequate? Are they performed on schedule?

The host employer will want to know what criteria the proposed contractor uses to hire subcontractors. Everything the host employer requires of the general contractor must be extended to the subcontractors. An example of this would be screening workers for drug and substance abuse.

Contract language should clearly spell out that the contractor agrees to comply with all federal, state and local safety regulations and with applicable consensus standards, such as ANSI A10.33, "Safety and Health Program Requirements for Multi-Employer Projects."

For maximum efficiency, the contractor should designate specific people to respond to the host employer's safety and health needs. These people should spearhead all of the contractor's safety-required activities, including:
- Prescreening workers and new hires for drug and substance abuse
- Verifying required training and/or certification
- Selecting and providing safety and health equipment and supplies
- Providing a safety and health orientation for the contract workers

110

If the contracted work is complex or performed during an extended period of time, the host employer's staff coordinator should monitor the contractor's safety performance periodically. The coordinator can perform safety inspections, review incident reports and have the contractor provide safety appraisals on a regular basis.

Verifying contractor insurance

Verification of contractor insurance is an essential part of an effective contractor control program. A request for proposal should include the requirement that the contractor provide appropriate certificates of insurance and amounts, to remain in force throughout the project. Before awarding the contract for a project, the host employer needs to review the potential for loss and establish minimum limits for insurance.

The host employer's coordinator verifies the coverage, noting and tracking any expiration dates. If the project takes longer than anticipated, the insurance must be checked to be sure it is still adequate and in force.

When appropriate, especially for long-term projects, the contract administrator of the host employer may require a contractor to state as part of the certificate of insurance that the owner is an additional name insured. In addition, the coordinator may want to check the qualifications of those who train the contractor's workers. In fact, the coordinator may even attend a training session to monitor its quality and appropriateness.

Training by the contractor for the contractor's workers also must be verified. The host employer should develop procedures to ensure that:

- Training needs have been identified
- Personnel who conduct training have the required qualifications
- Regulatory requirements have been met
- Records are adequately and accurately documented

In addition to safety and health training appropriate to the project, the contractor's workers must be trained in any special characteristics or hazards the site presents.

For instance, if they are working in areas with excessive noise exposure, have contract employees been provided with hearing protection by the contractor, and do they know how to use it properly? Do they know how to store and dispose of supplies and waste?

If the contractor's employees will be working near or with hazardous chemicals, do they know what those hazards are, how to protect themselves against them and what to do in case of a chemical accident or spill? Do they share information about chemicals they bring into the host's property? It is up to the host company to coordinate hazardous materials information among all contractors working on that site who might possibly be exposed. The host company also must train contractors on what the emergency plan calls for, what signals are given in an emergency and what the contractor's employees need to do to respond to that emergency.

For example, if a contractor's employees are given respirators to carry with them at all times, do those employees have the necessary training on how to use the respirators and how to evacuate the site? Does the contractor have a written respiratory protection program and a means to address all that it requires, including fitting, maintenance, medical assessment and cleaning? Audits are a tool to help verify that appropriate, timely training has taken place.

Element 6.4.3
Vendors

Vendors

In order to limit hazards introduced from the outside, companies need a proactive safety and health program in place to qualify purchases of various tools, equipment, materials and supplies and to monitor purchases from vendors for compliance.

As a first step in identifying risk exposure, companies need to regularly review the loss-producing potential of purchased products and services. In short, what can go wrong if these products fail or do not protect employees adequately? What are the financial implications if they fail? Hazards can be ranked by probability of occurrence and rated by severity of potential consequences as well as number of employees exposed.

Organizations should ensure that a pre-start-up safety review occurs prior to the start up of new process or equipment. On occasion, production pressures on project engineers may result in a failure to ensure that equipment or processes meet all safety requirements.

Companies should pay special attention to personal protective equipment purchases, such as eye protection and respirators. Other key elements to be assessed include ropes and chains for moving suspended loads and equipment to move and store materials. If chemicals create a hazard and cannot be replaced by non- or less-hazardous substances, then both the hazard and the exposure to the hazard must be controlled. Purchase specifications for substances used for cleaning or maintenance need to be reviewed to be sure the cleaners do not cause or aggravate fire and health hazards. If they do, and such cleaners are the only products available to do the job, then employees and others must be appropriately protected.

At a minimum, all purchasing agreements should clearly spell out the buyers' requirements. These requirements should reflect the equipment's intended use as well as any special conditions of the location where it will be used.

If the company operates in a global market, plans to do so, or buys from vendors outside the United States, its purchasing procedures also should take into account applicable international standards and directives as they are developed.

For maximum effectiveness in controlling external exposure from vendors, management needs cross-functional teamwork among safety and health professionals, plant operations personnel, engineers and purchasing agents. Answers to the following questions should be obtained:

- Is there a procedure that reviews the safety of materials, tools and equipment before they are bid on and purchased? Is the procedure periodically updated and evaluated for effectiveness?
- Is there a pre-start-up safety review of changes or commencing new operations? Are the operators or other experienced employees participating in these pre-start-up reviews?
- Are the plant's processes periodically reviewed, especially as markets and tech-

nology develop and change? Are ergonomic aspects considered when tools and equipment are selected?

- Can production processes be modified to minimize waste or reduce hazards of waste disposal? If so, have purchasing specifications been reviewed and, if necessary, changed to reflect those modifications?
- Does the company track and monitor phase-in dates or changes in regulatory requirements and are specifications for incoming products changed accordingly?
- If used machinery or equipment is purchased, has it been checked for safety? Does it comply with current OSHA and consensus standards? If end-user hardware for guarding is to be installed, is the type of guarding appropriate for how the machine will be used? Have guards been installed correctly?
- Have safe shipping methods been specified? Are all hazardous materials labeled with Department of Transportation-specified shipping labels? Do Material Safety Data Sheets accompany all incoming chemicals or products containing hazardous chemicals? Vendors must be required, if appropriate, to label incoming products with information meeting the requirements of the Hazard Communication Standard.

Companies can minimize their risk of exposure from vendors by controlling the quality of materials and services they purchase. To that end, management should establish a policy that any deviations from material specifications require the written permission of the engineering or design departments and that any deviations should be reviewed by a safety and health professional.

Management also should compile a list of "approved" suppliers and products, furnish suppliers with detailed requirements to avoid misunderstanding or misinterpretation, and develop procedures to monitor suppliers.

Product safety control

Product safety issues represent a significant financial risk for companies. Product liability affects not only industrial capital goods firms, but also manufacturers of consumer durables, such as autos and appliances, and industrial equipment and machinery companies. In addition, product safety concerns are issues for wholesalers, distributors, retailers, service, and repair organizations and various contracting firms. Adverse effects of product liability exposure can include:

- Plant closings
- Discontinuance of existing products
- Increased insurance costs
- Employee layoffs
- Loss of market share
- Termination of research on product lines judged liability-prone
- Decisions not to introduce newly developed products

Element 6.4.4

Products produced by the company

As a first step in minimizing exposure, management needs to understand all possible bases for claims and develop a comprehensive program addressing product safety issues.

A product is more than just the item sold. A product includes the sales literature, labels, manuals and advertising supplied with the item, attached to it, printed on it, or printed or sent separately after purchase. A product also includes the parts, accessories and special tools supplied by the manufacturer to the customer.

Once a product has been sold, it is a potential source of legal liability for the manufacturer or anyone else in the distribution chain if it is involved in an incident, injury or illness. Undesirable product incident exposure also can occur with products in use but no longer being manufactured.

Many areas of business activity have the potential for causing an incident that would put the company at risk. For instance, activities related to product concept, research, design, development and testing are possible sources of product liability claims, as are manufacturing and product quality assurance.

Claims can arise from a company's non-compliance with industry standards, regulations, codes and record-retention practices. Warnings, instructions and information should be checked. Advertising and representations, marketing and sales, and maintenance, service and repairs are additional risk exposures, as are packaging, shipping, storage and handling.

Because all these areas can be a potential source of loss for an organization, an effective program to identify risk exposure gathers and analyzes data from all operating components. Such data can include:

- Product safety hazard analysis
- Loss trends
- Warranty or guarantee claims
- Product incidents and claim history
- Production and sales volume, distribution data and utilization data as needed to accurately define the extent of possible future liability

Management can demonstrate commitment to a product safety program in several ways. A policy statement will make it clear that safety and the control of product liability losses are important company objectives. Such a policy statement should be communicated to all levels of management and all affected employees.

In addition, management needs to provide the leadership and resources necessary to implement the product safety program.

Many companies have chosen to set up product safety departments or to name a product safety coordinator. Legal and insurance specialists, either within the company or the retained attorney and insurance carrier, can be called on for help in developing a comprehensive product safety program.

Because no two companies operate the same way, there is no "best" way to organize such a program; however, a strong product safety program will include the following:

- Established guidelines and criteria to identify and evaluate product hazards and their associated potential for loss
- Basic procedures for design, development and testing of effective instructions and warning labels for product hazards that cannot be eliminated
- Established guidelines and review of all printed material to be sure it is clear and conforms to laws and regulations of all federal, state and local acts, codes and directives
- Notification of any federal, state or local regulatory agency if a product is defective or does not comply with safety standards, codes or regulations
- Development of written procedures for recalling products, notifying the public and correcting the problem

Public liability exposures

Element 6.4.5
Public liability

A company's plan to manage and control external exposures must include consideration of its public liability. If there is a reasonable expectation that the public will be exposed to a hazard created by, or arising, out of company activities, a company needs to foresee those risks and take appropriate action to minimize its public liability exposure. Failure to do so can result in substantial financial loss.

Fences, barricades and warning signs should control public access to hazardous areas such as construction sites. If company parking lots or sidewalks have holes, these should be fixed promptly. Excavations should be barricaded and fenced for the duration of construction work. Lighting must be adequate to identify hazards. Warning signs need to be posted.

Good housekeeping and order are "musts" for areas to which the public has access. For instance, in restaurants and stores, spills need to be cleaned promptly from floors and aisles need to be kept clear of obstructions.

Other public liability exposures are less apparent, yet management needs to be aware of responsibility for them. For example, company premises must be up-to-date in meeting life safety codes and standards set by such organizations as the National Fire Protection Association.

Waiting rooms, reception areas, cafeterias, restrooms, drinking fountains and elevators used by the public must comply with access requirements mandated by the Americans with Disabilities Act, or with consensus standards like American National Standards Institute, ANSI/CABO Al 17.1-1992 "Accessible and Usable Buildings and Facilities." People with mobility disabilities should be able to enter and leave the building easily; and exit signs must be clearly marked.

If companies invite private individuals onto their premises, management needs to be sure procedures are in place to keep visitors out of restricted areas in which heavy equipment is operating. Machines should be guarded; ramps, stairways and balconies also must be guarded properly.

Plant tours are another potential source of public liability. Visitors touring the facility should be provided with, and instructed, on the use of hard hats, safety glasses, hearing protection or safety footwear required to protect them against any hazards in the areas they may pass through.

A proactive approach to minimizing losses includes the assessment of potential liability. Management needs to know how serious a loss might be, so it can rank exposures and act accordingly. In short, management needs to ask:

- What can go wrong?
- What are the probabilities that something will go wrong?
- What would be the consequences if something does go wrong?

Companies must be sure all of their facilities comply fully with all requirements – not only to address the health and safety of employees and the community, but also to minimize public liability exposure in case of a disaster.

Element 6: Operational safety and health programs review

Issues/questions	In place			Action plan (if "no" or "partially")
	Yes	No	Partially	
1. Company safety and health policy mandates (at least) compliance with all federal, state and local standards.				
2. The organization has specific procedures in place identifying applicable regulations and tracking pending regulations.				
3. Compliance management has been delegated to a responsible department or individuals.				
4. Management understands the financial implications of non-compliance.				
5. Organization has a clear understanding of what implementing a safety management system requires.				
6. Adequate resources are allocated to assess compliance with mandatory standards and best practices.				
7. Management provides funds to subscribe to regulatory services, join associations and attend seminars to keep up to date on new regulations and standards.				
8. The organization periodically and regularly conducts self-assessments.				
9. If the organization conducts business outside the United States, it has contacted the relevant countries for regulatory information and guidance.				
10. Has management established a formal occupational health program?				
11. Has management hired or contacted with a physician, nurse and/or hygienists as needed?				

Element 6: Operational safety and health programs review

Issues/questions	In place			Action plan (if "no" or "partially")
	Yes	No	Partially	
12. Are hired or contracted occupational health personnel adequate in number, skills and training for workplace conditions?				
13. Are accurate and complete medical records maintained? Are procedures in place for notification and reports involving injuries, illnesses, fatalities and exposures within the company as required by regulatory bodies?				
14. Does management address the special needs of employees with disabilities?				
15. Has the organization identified chemical exposures that may lead to an occupational illness, such as cancer?				
16. Has the organization identified the biological exposures that may lead to an occupational illness, such as hepatitis infection?				
17. Has the organization identified the physical hazards that may lead to an occupational illness, such as hearing loss?				
18. Has the organization identified the ergonomic factors that may cause an occupational illness, such as a musculoskeletal disorder?				
19. Are exposures to illness-inducing risk factors evaluated?				
20. Are engineering controls instituted to control exposure to illness risk factors? Is personal protective equipment only used as a last resort or supplement?				
21. Are control methods for exposure to risk factors that may cause occupational illness regularly evaluated to determine their acceptance and effectiveness?				
22. Does management provide counseling on lifestyle problems through an employee assistance program?				

Element 6: Operational safety and health programs review

Issues/questions	In place			Action plan (if "no" or "partially")
	Yes	No	Partially	
23. Have medical examinations and medical surveillance needs been evaluated? Are procedures in place and effective?				
24. Are there established, effective procedures to insure confidentiality of medical records? Are records being maintained in compliance with the 30-year retention requirement?				
25. Has the organization implemented all safety programs required by regulatory requirements?				
26. Has the organization identified and implemented "best safety practices" that exceed the minimal regulatory requirements?				
27. Has the organization provided appropriate training so employees can fulfill their roles in the safety program?				
28. Is compliance with safety programs routinely monitored for levels of acceptance and effectiveness?				
29. Does the organization have an emergency plan that addresses a minimum of fire, natural disasters, medical emergencies, hazardous material releases, workplace violence and man-made crisis?				
30. Is the plan current? Are all employees trained in their emergency response roles?				
31. Are employees drilled using different emergency scenarios?				
32. Has the host employer set adequate guidelines for managing and controlling contractor programs? Have these guidelines been reviewed by the employers legal counsel and insurance representative?				
33. Has the company assessed and prioritized exposure risks by project and degree of risk? Are contractors prequalified?				

Element 6: Operational safety and health programs review

Issues/questions	In place			Action plan (if "no" or "partially")
	Yes	No	Partially	
34. Have contractors' insurance premium limits and conditions been predetermined for each project? Are insurance coverages verified independently and tracked for expiration dates?				
35. Are procedures in place to monitor and update purchasing specifications to reflect changes and modifications in regulations, standards and international directives?				
36. Does the company furnish suppliers with detailed requirements to avoid misunderstanding or misinterpretation?				
37. Has the company developed and implemented a comprehensive product safety program? Have legal counsel and insurance carriers participated in designing, developing, monitoring and updating the program?				
38. Are good housekeeping and order "musts" for all areas to which the public has access? Are appropriate maintenance and inspection procedures developed, followed and monitored?				
39. Is risk exposure periodically reviewed with legal counsel and insurance carriers? Are appropriate insurance coverages in force and monitored for expiration dates?				
40. Has senior management reviewed disaster risk assessment - not only for normal conditions, but also for "what if" scenarios and "worst case" disasters?				
41. Has senior management named and appropriately trained a senior official and a backup person to deal with disasters? Does the official have authority to make immediate or timely decisions in the event of a disaster? Are funds and personnel available on a timely basis to implement those decisions?				

Element 6: Operational safety and health programs review

Issues/questions	In place			Action plan (if "no" or "partially")
	Yes	No	Partially	
42. Have primary and contingency plans that comply with all applicable regulations been developed to protect persons, property, operations and the environment? To restore business operations? Have the plans been clearly communicated to management, employees, and appropriate community and government agencies?				
43. Have funds and staff been committed for training and refresher training as needed? Is record keeping adequate to document required training?				
44. Are plans periodically monitored, reviewed and updated as appropriate? Is required information on file with appropriate agencies?				

element 7

employee involvement

Element 7: Employee involvement

7.1 Management has a policy or other documents identifying employee involvement as an element vital to the success of a safety management system. The documentation identifies specific employee involvement goals, activities and benefits that the organization expects to derive from those activities.

    7.1.1 The organization has identified benefits expected from employee involvement activities.

    7.1.2 The organization has identified specific goals for levels of employee involvement. The goal may be a specified number of employees, a specified number of activities or implementation of actions identified as gaps through the assessment process.

7.2 Management has a policy or other documents identifying site-specific employee involvement tools used in its safety management system. Included are the following elements:

    7.2.1 Individual development and training

    7.2.2 Individual involvement and influence

    7.2.3 Constant and varied communication

    7.2.4 At-risk behavior auditing

    7.2.5 Recognition and reward

    7.2.6 Appropriate hazard recognition tools such as:

        7.2.6.1 Job safety analysis

        7.2.6.2 Physical hazard inspections

        7.2.6.3 Employee safety training

        7.2.6.4 Safety meetings

        7.2.6.5 Job safety observations

        7.2.6.6 Safety committees or teams

Overview

Employee involvement is critical to the effective functioning of any safety management system. After visible management leadership and commitment, no other element dictates the final format and the ultimate success of the site-specific safety management system, as does meaningful employee involvement.

While it is vital that all of the management team be visibly engaged in the daily functioning of the safety management system, it is equally critical that the hourly workforce also be engaged in shaping the safety management system. Examples of activities that engage the workforce include safety meetings, safety training, job safety analysis, job safety observations or functioning as member of a specialized team, such as an emergency response team or a joint safety committee.

Employee involvement is not an altruistic concept. Both organizations and employees reap a variety of tangible and intangible benefits from a workforce that is actively engaged in the safety management system. Increased employee morale, increased efficiencies through workable safe-operating procedures, identification of training needs, and an increased employee stake in the operation of the safety management system are all benefits derived from employee involvement. The most notable benefit is the increased probability that safety measures developed and implemented with employee involvement will be effective, will be adhered to and will result in decreased injuries and illnesses.

Employee involvement

Rarely is a safety professional able to implement changes or modify procedures without seeking permission from higher authority within the organization. It is even rarer for employees affected by changes to their work environment to adhere to such changes unless they understand how they benefit from the change.

Effective safety professionals must explain how proposed changes will benefit the employee. To increase salaried and hourly employee support for employee involvement activities, management must make clear the benefits of these activities to the organization and to individual employees.

Benefits of involvement

Some of the benefits of employee involvement that may be expected include:

- **Early identification of uncontrolled hazards in the workplace.** Employees are often the first to be keenly aware of changes in the work environment or hazards that may impact their well being. Employee involvement activities usually provide additional avenues for controlling such hazards before an injury occurs. The employees benefit by maintaining their health.
- **The organization benefits as the controls for these hazards are implemented.** Controlled hazards are less likely to result in an employee injury. Fewer employee injuries mean lower expenses because of fewer injury-related expenses or lower workers' compensation premiums. Lower expenses benefit the organization

Element 7.1

Management has a policy or other documents that identify employee involvement as an element vital to the success of a safety management system. The documentation identifies specific employee involvement goals, activities and benefits the organization expects to derive from those activities.

Element 7.1.1

The organization has identified benefits expected from employee involvement activities.

through increased profits. Increased profits also benefit the employees, as they tend to result in greater job security and increased likelihood of employee raises.

- **Identification of training needs.** Employees benefit by receiving skills and knowledge that allow them to perform their job safely. Employees also benefit by not being required to attend unnecessary training.
- **The organization benefits as resources are directed to situations where training needs exist.** Funds and resources are not wasted sending employees to irrelevant or redundant training.
- **Identification of safe operating procedures.** Employees benefit by being able to influence the procedures that will be used as standard operating procedures. When experienced employees are allowed to participate in the development process, the procedures developed tend to be more readily followed and to be more workable than procedures developed by individuals who are less familiar with the daily requirements of the worker and the task.
- **The organization benefits as best safety practices are identified and standardized throughout the organization.** These best safety practices tend to result in increased operating efficiencies as well as fewer injuries.
- **Increase in employee morale.** Employees who are able to influence their work environment tend to report higher levels of job satisfaction. Studies indicate that employees who report higher levels of job satisfaction tend to be more productive. Organizations benefit through a lower level of absenteeism and lower turnover costs associated with replacing departed employees.

Involvement goals

Element 7.1.2
The organization has identified specific goals for levels of employee involvement. The goal may be a specified number of employees, a specified number of activities or implementation of actions identified as gaps through the assessment process.

Meaningful employee involvement is a critical component in influencing an organization's overall safety culture. When employees are engaged in the safety management system, they become keenly aware of the actions the organization is taking to enhance their personal safety and health. Stories of decisions made to protect their safety and priorities given in implementing a safety management system spread by word of mouth. These stories support statements by the management team indicating the organization is committed to protecting the safety of the employees. Employee involvement does not happen by chance or through the good intentions of a management team. Like any other organization goal, employee involvement is best achieved through careful planning.

Some organizations state their employee organization goal as a percentage of overall workforces. Other organizations state their goals in terms of activities such as number of inspections conducted by department employees or number of safety teams. Some employers base their employee involvement goals in terms of implementation of proactive programs indicated through assessments.

For example, an organization may assess its current state by using the nine elements of a safety management system. Gaps identified could be addressed through implementation of specific actions by employees.

Some considerations in planning for employee involvement include:

• **Start small then build on success.** If employee involvement is a new concept to an organization, it is better to start small and build on successes. For example, an organization with no formal inspection procedure in place sets a goal to have all employees participate in at least one safety inspection per year. It may be better to start off by developing inspection teams in a limited number of departments. This will allow the organization to respond to unexpected issues that may arise.

For example, the hazards reported through these inspections may require changes within the maintenance department. The inspections also may require changes in communication methods so the employees may track the status of abatement of reported hazards.

As another example, a company sets an employee involvement goal to have each supervisor work with three employees to develop one job safety analysis once a quarter. This may be a waste of company resources if a completed job safety analysis is not incorporated into the department routine. In addition, this could send a negative message to the employees. By starting with a few supervisor/employee teams and then addressing issues that arise, the employee involvement can be effective in strengthening the safety management system.

Employee involvement does not consist of doing meaningless tasks whose results are largely ignored. Meaningful employee involvement means the results of these activities are used to impact the workplace in a positive manner.

• **Solicit opinion leaders' support before initiating employee involvement activities.** Different roles are formed anytime a group of people work together. Opinion leaders are those individuals within the group upon whom the other employees rely to guide their own opinions. Opinion leaders may be formally recognized by the group in elected positions, such as union stewards. Opinion leaders also may be individuals whose personal credibility within the group causes their opinions to be sought out and mirrored by other individuals within the group.

Opinion leaders are easily identified when some change impacts the group. Effective safety professionals will meet with opinion leaders before implementing any large-scale changes. The meeting should explain the need for the change, expected benefits of the change, address concerns of opinion leaders and solicit their support. When opinion leaders support change, the changes tend to be incorporated more smoothly into the workplace.

• **Evaluate the benefits of any employee involvement activity on an ongoing basis.** The National Safety Council defines occupational safety as the control and elimination of recognized hazards to attain an acceptable level of risk. Within this simple definition are three critical components that may be used to evaluate safety activities, such as employee involvement tools. When considering safety activities or employee involvement activities consider:

1. Does this activity control or eliminate a hazard?
2. Does this activity teach an employee to recognize a hazard the employee would have otherwise not been aware of?
3. Does this activity alter what an individual believes is an acceptable level of risk? In other words, is some behavior or action different after the employee involvement activity than before the employee involvement activity occurred?

If the answers to those three questions are all "no," a safety professional should question the value of such an employee involvement activity.

Safety professionals also should periodically evaluate the effectiveness of ongoing employee involvement activities. Sometimes activities lose effectiveness through time. It may be better to have a variety of activities that different employees engage in for a period of months than a single activity that goes on without end. For example, a committee may be formed to address a specific concern or project, and then be disbanded after the concern or project is resolved.

As another example, a supervisor has a safety meeting one month, conducts a safety inspection with his employees the following month and develops a job safety analysis for a department task the following month. This variety may have a greater impact on controlling and eliminating recognized hazards or altering what an employee believes is an acceptable level of risk than month after month of safety meetings.

Organizations commit resources in supporting employee involvement activities. The safety professional should be able to show tangible results from this resource allocation.

- **Celebrate successes.** Many organizations make the mistake of using injury rates as an employee motivation tool. There are many flaws with this approach.

 Injury rates are lagging indicators. A zero injury rate does not always mean an effective safety management system is in place. And it is possible that injuries are going unreported.

 Rather, a safety management system improves as an organization implements changes that control or eliminate hazards, that teach employees to recognize hazards or that alter what employees believe is an acceptable level of risk. As organizations implement the meaningful employee involvement activities, the safety management system improves. It is appropriate to celebrate these improvements.

 Some organizations have moved toward celebrating every time 100 hazards are abated as opposed to celebrating a goal associated with the injury rate. Other organizations celebrate team-completed specific projects. It is appropriate that these activities be celebrated throughout the facility.

 These celebrations reinforce the fact that management has committed time and resources to safety. These celebrations acknowledge that other employees covered the workload of those who were engaged in these employee involvement activities. And these celebrations move away from a system that rewards lagging indicators that are not under the individual's immediate control, such as injury rates, to a system that rewards proactive measures in which an individual can participate.

If the employee involvement tools are properly implemented as part of the overall safety management system, the injury rate will be reduced through time.

Individual employee involvement

Every employee is both entitled to, and responsible for, safety and health in the workplace regardless of whether the individual is engaged in some specific employee involvement activity. Management should support individual efforts by providing clear expectations, facilitating employee input and acknowledging individual achievements.

A safety and health management system includes a definition and assignment of safety and health responsibility and accountability for all levels of management and all employees. This establishes what is expected of both management and employees in terms of their roles in the safety and health management system; it is the first step in enlisting individual involvement. The employee's basic responsibilities should include:

- Demonstrated knowledge of all behaviors required to comply with all company safety and health requirements (practices and procedures)
- Demonstrated ability to respond in an emergency
- Demonstrated commitment to ask for help when unsure of how to perform any task safely
- Demonstrated commitment to report unsafe practices and hazardous work conditions and procedures

Management underpins employee responsibility by also establishing accountability for safety and health. Each employee's contribution to workplace safety should be considered in the assessment of his or her overall job performance.

Development and training

It is critical that management support the individual by providing training appropriate to the expected behaviors. Training is required to give an individual the skills or knowledge necessary to complete the expected tasks or responsibilities.

Too often, expectations are developed without providing the employee the training required to succeed. Consider an individual who is promoted from the workforce to the position of a first line supervisor. Sometimes that individual is expected to complete incident investigations, conduct safety meetings and lead hazard inspections as part of his or her new job responsibilities. Too often, those tasks are expected to be completed in a professional manner even though the recently promoted individual was provided no training. The result is often frustration and a shying away from safety responsibilities.

In summary, there should be a clear listing of safety-related roles and behaviors listed for each employee position, and a clear plan indicating how individuals will be trained to succeed in the required roles and behaviors.

Element 7.2

Management has a policy or other documents identifying site-specific employee involvement tools used in its safety management system.

Element 7.2.1

Individual development and training

129

Individual involvement and influence

Each employee may have ideas to contribute to the improvement of the safety and health management system in their workplace. Management and staff professionals should acknowledge this by establishing systems that elicit individual input on an ongoing basis.

An employee suggestion system allows employees to contribute their suggestions and opinions in writing via an established procedure. Organizations report varying degrees of success in using the employee suggestion system. The most successful use of an employee suggestion system occurs in those organizations in which the suggestions are responded to quickly and employees are recognized for contributing to the betterment of the safety management system.

Responding to an employee suggestion does not mean the suggestion was necessarily implemented. Responding to the suggestion means the employee received feedback as to why the suggestion will or will not be implemented. Employees will continue to support a suggestion system if such feedback is received. Few employees will participate in an employee suggestion system if some of the suggestions are ignored without any comment back to the initiator.

Many organizations have moved away from employee suggestion systems to a more active method of involving the individual employee. One method involves a one-on-one, safety-related meeting between Supervisor and employee after job safety observations or as part of a job safety analysis (JSA). (See 7.2.6.1) After observing the employee at work, the supervisor takes the opportunity to both recognize and reinforce safe job performance, and to correct at-risk behaviors and offer further instruction as necessary. The employee, on the other hand, is given the opportunity to voice opinions regarding his or her own performance and company safety and health rules, procedures and programs in a forum where he or she is assured of being heard.

Job safety analysis (JSA) formally allows employees to participate in identifying hazards and unsafe practices in the workplace and modify work methods to prevent injury illness and incidents and improve productivity and product quality. This process encourages safe work practices on a personal level because it relies on employee expertise and knowledge about each job and its related tasks. When used as a tool for continuous improvement, job safety analysis facilitates better communication between line employees, supervisors and senior managers.

Safety and health meetings are most often thought of as a means of training and disseminating safety and health information to employees, but these meetings also can be a forum for soliciting employee input. The downfall of many safety meetings is that they are regarded as obligatory, both by the presenter and the audience. Just holding a safety meeting does not guarantee that safety and health are addressed in a manner that is meaningful to employees.

The meeting should be well planned around a topic that is truly relevant to the well being of those attending. It should be presented in an organized manner by a supervisor, team member, staff member or consulting professional who is well prepared and well versed in the discussion topic. Finally, time should be allotted at the conclusion of the presentation for feedback and questions from the audience. A detailed agenda, circulated in advance to the target audience, allows those attending to prepare themselves to participate.

Perception surveys are a means of giving all employees a voice in the direction of the safety and health management system. The overall safety and health management system cannot be truly effective unless it is perceived as having value, and acted on accordingly, by employees.

These surveys quantify the attitudes that influence acceptance and safe job performance. A company- or facility-wide perception survey can pinpoint program inadequacies and credibility gaps in management's commitment to safety. Moreover, because surveys are anonymous and administered to all levels, all employees have an equal voice – even those who might be unable or unwilling to voice dissatisfaction in other circumstances. Results of the survey must be made known to all participants in a timely manner.

Constant and varied communications

In order to maintain a high level of interest in employee involvement activities, employees have to perceive some value being derived from that activity. Communication is vital in maintaining employee interest.

Consider the following example: An employee reports a potential hazard. The hazard is evaluated and is determined to have a low probability of occurrence with a low level of severity. This hazard will be addressed, but the resources of the facility are currently directed toward abating another hazard that has a much greater probability of occurring with a much higher level of severity if the hazard occurs. It is critical that the employee who reported the hazard of lesser severity be given timely information on the status of the hazard reported.

Employees understand organizations have limited resources and understand priority systems. Employees will continue to support a safety management system when their requests are responded to in timely manner. Employees will not continue to engage in activities where their requests are ignored.

Further, communicating an improvement that only impacts one department in the facility to all employees in all departments reinforces management commitment to employee involvement in the safety management system.

Communications are often most effective when the supervisor speaks directly with the employee. But verbal communication should be supplemented with written communications posted in communication centers or other methods reinforcing the verbal communication.

At-risk behavior auditoring

Traditionally, safety professionals group causes of injuries as either unsafe acts or

Element 7.2.3
Constant and varied communications

Element 7.2.4
At-risk behavior auditing

unsafe behaviors. Many of the traditional safety efforts, such as physical hazard inspections and writing work orders, tend to focus on unsafe conditions. In an effective safety management system, there is some formal system in place that addresses unsafe behaviors.

There may be resistance to at-risk behavior auditing as some employees may feel it is a way of blaming the employee. When at-risk behavior auditing is properly understood, it is apparent that the behaviors exhibited have less to do with individual employees and more to do with the behaviors the entire management system either condones or outright encourages. Employees perform in manner consistent with the safety culture created by the actual values, beliefs and principles demonstrated by the management team.

At-risk behavior auditing requires that task-related behaviors critical to site safety performance be identified and employees are trained and equipped to perform these behaviors in the prescribed manner. Job safety analysis are often a useful tool in identifying these behaviors.

At-risk behavior auditing addresses exposure to injury that occurs in the completion of specific job tasks. The number of safe and at-risk behaviors can be tracked as a measure of overall performance or impact of specific safety training. Many organizations find that reducing the number of at-risk behaviors has had the desired effect of reducing injury rates.

Element 7.2.5

Recognition and reward

Recognition and reward

Employees who participate in employee involvement activities should receive some form of recognition consistent with their contributions. When this recognition comes in conjunction with peer-attended celebrations, such as lunches, it tends to reinforce the commitment of management to the safety management system and reinforce the value of employee involvement activities.

Recognition does not always have to come in the form of a gift or tangible item given to employees. One of the most powerful forms of recognition can be sincere gratitude for their efforts expressed by their immediate supervisor.

Element 7.2.6

Activity-based hazard recognition and abatement tools

Activity-based recognition

The organization should incorporate a variety of activity-based hazard recognition tools into its safety management system.

Element 7.2.6.1

Job safety analysis

Job safety analysis

Job safety analysis is the foundation for the proactive identification of workplace hazards. This tool breaks jobs down into smaller tasks that are then analyzed to recognize hazards. Job safety analysis provides important benefits, including setting performance standards included in standard operating procedures, providing planned safety observation data, facilitating training and integrating safety into production functions.

Job Safety Analysis (JSA) Form

∷nsc
National Safety Council

Job safety analysis
Instructions on reverse side

Company/Organization:

Plant/location:

Required and/or recommended personal protective equipment:

Job title (and number if applicable):

Page ____ of ____ JSA no. ____

☐ New
☐ Revised

Date:

Title of person who does job:

Supervisor:

Department:

Analysis by:

Reviewed by:

Approved by:

Sequence of basic job steps	Hazards	Recommended action or procedure

Source: National Safety Council

133

Instructions for completing the Job Safety Analysis (JSA) Form

The Job Safety Analysis (JSA) is an important analyzing tool that works by finding hazards in a job and eliminating or minimizing them before the job is performed. Use the JSA for job clarification and hazard awareness, for periodic one-on-one safety-related meetings and for retraining senior employees, as a guide in new employee training and as a refresher on jobs that run infrequently. It also can be used as an incident investigation tool.

Set priorities for doing job safety analysis. Conduct analysis on jobs that have a history of causing injury or damage, that have produced disabling injuries, with high potential for disabling injury or death and on new jobs.

Select a job to be analyzed. Before filling out the form, consider the purpose of the job, the activities it involves and the hazards it presents. If unfamiliar with a particular job or operation, interview an employee who performs the job. In addition, observing an employee performing the job, or "walking through" the operation step-by-step may give additional insight into potential hazards. Videotaping can be used to help analysis.

There are three main parts to the job safety analysis form — outlining the sequence of basic job steps, identifying potential hazards, and summarizing recommended actions or procedures.

Sequence of basic job steps

Examining a specific job by breaking it down into a series of steps or tasks, will allow discovery of potential hazards employees may encounter. Each job or operation will consist of a set of steps or tasks.

For example, the job might be to move a box from a conveyor in the receiving area to a shelf in the storage area. To determine where a step begins or ends, look for a change of activity, change in direction or movement.

Picking up the box from the conveyor and placing it on a hand truck is one step. The next step might be to push the loaded hand truck to the storage area, representing a change in activity. Moving the box from the truck to the shelf is another step. The final step might be returning the hand truck to the receiving area.

When completing the form, be sure to list all the steps needed to perform the job. Some steps may not be performed each time. In the example above, a step that isn't performed every time might be checking the casters on the hand truck; however, if that step is generally part of the job it should be listed.

Hazards

A hazard is a potential danger. The purpose of the JSA is to identify all hazards - those produced by the environment or conditions and those connected with the job procedure.

To identify hazards, the following questions should be asked for each step of the job:
- Is there a danger of the employee striking against, being struck by, or otherwise making injurious contact with an object?
- Can the employee be caught in, by or between objects?
- Is there potential for slipping, tripping or falling?
- Could the employee suffer strains from pushing, pulling, lifting, bending or twisting?
- Is the environment hazardous to safety and health, in terms of toxic gas, vapor, mist, fumes, dust, heat or radiation?

Close observation and knowledge of the job is important. Examine each step carefully to find and identify hazards - the actions, conditions and possibilities that could lead to injury, illness or damage. Compiling an accurate and complete list of hazards will facilitate the development of recommended safe job procedures.

Recommended action or procedure

Using the first two columns of the JSA form as a guide, decide what actions or procedures are necessary to eliminate or minimize the hazards that could lead to injury, illness or damage.

Begin by trying, in order, to:
1. Engineer out the hazards.
2. Provide guards and other safety devices.
3. Provide personal protective equipment.
4. Provide job instruction training.
5. Maintain good housekeeping.

Ensure good ergonomics by positioning the person in relation to the machine or other elements in such a way as to improve safety.

List the recommended safe-operating procedures. Begin with an action word, stating exactly what needs to be done to correct the hazard. An example is "Lift using your leg muscles." Avoid general statements such as "Be careful."

List the required or recommended personal protective equipment necessary to perform each step of the job. Give a recommended action or procedure for each hazard.

Serious hazards should be corrected immediately. The job safety analysis should then be changed to reflect the new conditions.

Finally, review all three columns for accuracy and completeness. Determine if the recommended actions or procedures have been put in place. Reevaluate the JSA as necessary.

Managing the JSA process

Job safety analysis follows a three-stage process for analyzing a specific job to identify and abate hazards. This is a participatory process requiring input, feedback and cooperative effort from production employees, supervisors and management.

1. **Preparing for the job safety analysis process**
   - Educate management and foster commitment.
   - Establish realistic expectations, roles and responsibilities and a measurement system.
   - Provide necessary training.

2. **Developing the job safety analysis**
   - Break job tasks into sequential steps.
   - Identify hazards related to these steps.
   - Specify control measures to reduce the hazards.

3. **Managing the continuous improvement process**
   - Use the completed job safety analysis as a guideline for continuously improving safe work practices and to facilitate continued involvement, communication and safety process improvement through meaningful employee involvement.

Element 7.2.6.2

Physical hazard inspections

Physical hazard inspections

More commonly known as a safety inspection, a physical hazard inspection is the second employee involvement tool. Safety inspections are regularly completed at most organizations. Applying this hazard-recognition tool to employee involvement means having production workers directly involved in the inspections.

Through time, *all* employees should be involved with physical hazard inspections and learn how to recognize hazards in the workplace.

Developing inspection checklists also includes employees within the various departments. Operators have a built-in "buy-in" to the process and know the reason for completing this activity.

Element 7.2.6.3

Employee safety training

Employee Safety Training

The third tool – employee safety training – provides the skills and knowledge required to complete job tasks without injury or property damage. Safety training is enhanced through the completion of job safety analysis. Information from the analysis is integrated into the standard operating procedures that in turn are used to develop operator job-instruction training programs. Employee safety training also includes regulatory training, such as hazard communication, confined space and lockout/tagout.

Element 7.2.6.4

Safety meetings

Safety meetings

There are several types of safety meetings – the fourth tool. Two of the more common types are department meetings and toolbox safety meetings.

136

Department meetings at most companies are held on a regular schedule, such as monthly or bi-weekly. These safety meetings provide communication and safety issue reviews, and may be a part of regular production meetings.

Toolbox safety meetings are held more frequently than department meetings. A first-line supervisor more often holds them. These meetings may be used as regular safety contacts between the first-line supervisor and workers. Before beginning work, toolbox safety meetings may be used for specific jobs or task reviews.

Safety meetings should be used to:
- Orient individuals on safety and health techniques and philosophy.
- Empower employees as problem-solvers and decision-makers.
- Identify and correct hazards through review of job safety analysis, inspections and observations.
- Develop leadership skills as facilitators.

Safety meetings should be planned and follow these guidelines:
- Use an agenda.
- Limit topics to three major issues.
- Discuss current relevant topics.
- Define expectations and roles, including management.
- Rotate leadership/facilitation.
- Set and follow a realistic pace.
- Follow up with action steps from the meeting action plan.

Job safety observations

The final tool is the job safety observation. Also known as job behavior observation, job safety observation is a process of observing an employee as he or she completes his or her work. This observation process is a means of determining if job training has been effective. Job training is based on work instructions that include job safety analysis information. Job safety observations can use the job safety analysis or work instructions as a tool to develop the job safety observation forms.

In addition to determining strengths and weaknesses in the employee's work knowledge, this process allows for the correction of inappropriate or at-risk behavior. It also allows for the reinforcement of correct work-completion actions.

A first-line supervisor, manager or peer worker may complete job safety observations using checklists. The most effective programs use all three observers.

The data from these observations may be collated and analyzed to determine workplace strengths and weaknesses. These areas of identified weakness can be used to improve the job instruction training. Ultimately, this process improves the knowledge of the employee and encourages the proper completion of future tasks.

Element 7.2.6.5

Job safety observations

137

Sample job safety observation form

Department : Warehouse	Supervisor: Tom Smith	Date:
Job Task: lamp replacement	Location/shift: shipping	

Catergory:	Safe	At-risk	Comments:
1. Procedures			
a. Hand hold while driving			
b. Driving with clear field of vision			
c. Conduct a lockout/tagout			
d. Changing bulb with two hands			
e. Testing bulb with area cleared			
Total (1)			
2. Tools and equipment			
a. Pre-walk-around			
b. Check controls			
c. Required replacement lamp			
Total (2)			
3. Physical conditions			
a. Use safety cones to secure area			
b. Floor conditions evaluated			
c. Placement and leveling of work platform			
Total (3)			
4. Personal protective equipment			
a. Hard hat			
b. Full face shield			
c. Safety glasses			
d. Fall protection			
e. Protective footwear			
f. Leather gloves			
Total (4)			

Overall (1 through 4)		
Calculations	Safe + At-risk = Total	Percent unsafe = At-risk/total x 100 =

Source: National Safety Council

Safety committees or teams

Several types of committees or teams may exist inside a facility. Some teams, such as joint safety committees, may be mandated by labor contracts or by state law. These committees may exist as a permanent function with the facility.

Other committees may serve a very specialized function within the organization, then be disbanded. One example of this type of committee might be an ergonomics team formed to resolve musculoskeletal disorders on a specific production line. Once effective engineering controls are installed or design changes incorporated into the process and appropriate training and reinforcement occur, this team may be disbanded.

Another example of a temporary team within an organization might be a team whose function is to incorporate safety into a new production line. After the pre-start-up safety review is completed and the line is routinely performing at an acceptable level of risk, this team may be disbanded.

Other specialized teams may exist as a permanent function within the facility. An example of this type of team would be the facility emergency response team.

Element 7.2.6.6

Safety committees or teams

Element 7: Employee involvement review

Issues/questions	In place			Action plan (if "no" or "partially")
	Yes	No	Partially	
1. Does a policy statement or other documentation mandate employee involvement as a critical element to the safety management system?				
2. Has the organization identified the specific benefits it will derive from employee involvement activities?				
3. Has the organization set goals for employee involvement in terms of specific number of employees, specific actions to take to improve the safety management system or specific employee involvement tools?				
4. Has the organization designated budget resources including scheduling time for employee involvement activities?				
5. Does the organization have development plans for employees to give them the skills and knowledge necessary to fulfill their individual roles?				
6. Does the organization have planned evaluations of the individual designed to assess additional training needs?				
7. Does the organization have prescribed methods that are used to solicit input, concerns and feedback from employees who are not actively engaged in some employee involvement activity?				
8. Are supervisors and other employees trained to use safety contacts as a method of engaging employees in the safety management system?				
9. Does the organization have effective communication methods that ensure follow-up and feedback to employees expressing concerns?				
10. Does the organization have a variety of written, verbal and visual methods in place that communicate employee activity status and successes?				

Element 7: Employee involvement review

Issues/questions	In place			Action plan (if "no" or "partially")
	Yes	No	Partially	
11. Has the organization developed safe operating procedures or identified critical behaviors for at-risk behavior auditing?				
12. Does the organization train employees on how to conduct at risk behavior audits in a positive manner?				
13. Does the organization use results of at-risk behavior audits for planning and intervention?				
14. Are individual employees given opportunities to voice opinions/concerns (meetings, surveys, suggestion system, safety and health contacts, JSAs, etc.)?				
15. Does management give formal recognition to individual and/or group contributions to safety and health?				
16. Does the organization promote and celebrate completion of projects and team efforts that strengthen the safety management system?				
17. Has the organization selected appropriate hazard recognition tools, such as job safety analysis, physical hazard inspections, committees, safety meetings, etc. for increasing employee involvement?				
18. Has the organization provided training to employees regarding the hazard recognition tools?				
19. Are the results of hazard recognition tools incorporated into the daily operating routine of the organization?				
20. Are employee involvement activities routinely evaluated to determine their continuing effectiveness?				

element 8

motivation, behavior and attitudes

Element 8: Motivation, behavior and attitudes

8.1 Management uses motivation to change employee behavior and attitudes. Motivation is defined by three variables:

    8.1.1 Direction of behavior

    8.1.2 Intensity of action

    8.1.3 Persistence of effort

8.2 Management uses motivational approaches to improve safety and health performance.

    8.2.1 The organization behavior management (OBM) model uses reinforcement and feedback to modify behavior.

    8.2.2 The total quality management (TQM) model uses attitude adjustment methods to achieve quality improvement goals in industry.

8.3 Management provides visible leadership to change employee attitudes and behaviors.

Overview

Motivation involves moving people to act in support of achieving desired goals. In occupational safety and health, motivation increases the awareness, interest and willingness of employees to act in ways that increase safety and that support an organization's safety goals and objectives.

Motivation changes behavior and attitudes in three ways: the direction of the behavior, the intensity of the action and the persistence of the effort.

Management uses two general approaches to motivate employees to improve safety and health performance. One, the organization behavior management model, uses reinforcement and feedback to modify behavior. The other, the total quality management model, adjusts attitudes to achieve quality improvement goals.

But the ultimate success of a motivational model in changing employee attitudes and behavior is directly related to visible management leadership. In addition, the motivational techniques used should support the mainline safety and health management system, not take its place. Similarly, evaluation of motivational techniques should be measured in terms of maintaining employees' interest in safety, rather than merely by the effect on injury rates. There are three specific motivational techniques: communications; incentives, awards and recognition, and employee surveys.

Motivation and behavior

Element 8.1

Management uses motivation to change employee behavior and attitudes.

The term motivation refers to the effect of attitude and behavior on how and why people adopt new behaviors or change old ones. Some experts believe motivation is best achieved by focusing on external behavior change, while others believe internal attitude or cognitive change must occur first. In everyday language, the word motivation refers to a variety of external and internal "pushes" and "pulls" that help to explain people's actions.

These concepts can be applied to occupational safety and health. For example, safety professionals discuss the need to "motivate" management to support the safety and health system or to "motivate" employees to follow safe job procedures. These professionals are seeking ways to change the behaviors and attitudes of people to meet defined safety goals.

Defining factors of motivation

Three factors define motivation – direction of behavior, intensity of action and persistence of effort.

Element 8.1.1

Direction of behavior

Direction of behavior relates to actions that accomplish defined objectives. To change the direction of behavior, management must first specify the behavior to be achieved. Then, employees must clearly understand how to achieve the desired objective.

Safety and health objectives can be defined very narrowly in terms of specific behaviors, or broadly in terms of process improvements. Once objectives have been set, employees must obtain the knowledge necessary to achieve those objectives. Unless management identifies desired behavior and employees understand how to achieve that behavior, motivational efforts are futile.

Intensity of action is the amount of personal attention and thought given to performing goal-oriented actions. Translated, this means employees integrate safety and health objectives into their job assignments with the same degree of mental and emotional effort they expend for other work objectives.

It also implies employees may have to spend extra time to incorporate safety and health practices into routine work patterns and, if necessary, accept the potentially bothersome aspects of some new behaviors that may be required.

Management must reinforce appropriate safety behaviors and strong performance levels to ensure employees are seriously involved. It also is critical that management communicate performance results to employees to demonstrate achievement and to emphasize the importance of performance to the organization.

Persistence of effort results in desired performance through time. Persistence of effort relates directly to the nurturing and maturing of the attitudes or actions that support improved safety and health performance throughout the organization. For this continuity of purpose to occur, both employees and management must be committed. Employees must be willing to modify personal behavior in accordance with company safety goals and objectives. Management must be visibly committed and active in its support for employee safety and health.

Company operating policies, rules and procedures normally address general safety practices. OSHA and related laws specify selected areas of compliance. Corporate culture also tends to influence safety priorities.

Often, however, the information from these sources is not sufficiently specific to cover the complete array of tasks that must be performed at the most basic operational levels. Furthermore, policies, rules and regulatory standards seldom, by themselves, carry the motivational impact necessary to affect safe job performance on a continuing basis. The first step to motivating employees is to set and clearly state safety objectives – defining the appropriate behaviors expected of employees.

Element 8.2

Management uses motivational approaches to improve safety and health performance.

Specifying safety objectives

Management should examine incident investigations and periodic inspections and audits for additional understanding of workplace safety needs and improvement opportunities. These procedures frequently pinpoint safety deficiencies in a concrete way and with an immediacy that directly influences employees to change their behaviors and improve their performance.

For example, the following behaviors are critical to preventing hazards:
- Operating equipment to maximize safe performance
- Adhering to work procedures that maximize safe performance
- Avoiding actions that increase risk of injury or illness

- Recognizing physical and process-related hazards
- Observing good housekeeping, maintenance and personal hygiene practices

Similarly, the following behaviors are critical to incident mitigation:
- Using personal protective equipment and other controls properly and consistently
- Recognizing illness-related symptoms
- Responding to emergency situations properly

In setting safety objectives, management should seek employee involvement in identifying and formulating safety needs to stimulate safe behavior. For example, the job safety analysis – which allows employees to participate in identifying hazards and creating elimination methods – lays an important foundation for behavior change. Management should reinforce such employee participation.

In addition, management should create an atmosphere of open communication and discussion by employees about safety and should respond to suggestions with corrective action when problems or hazards are reported. In this regard, the use of employee safety program perception and attitude assessments can play a significant role both in specifying process safety priorities and in enhancing employee morale.

Once safety improvement objectives are specified, employees must learn how to attain them. Training or retraining of employees is often a necessary step at this juncture of the improvement process and lays the groundwork for immediate positive results. With the proper thrust and scope, training in hazard identification and other skills also can develop an employee's capacity to make knowledgeable contributions to improved job safety performance.

Reinforcing desired behaviors

Once safety objectives are defined and employees know the behaviors necessary to attain them, these objectives and behaviors must become part of the pattern of performing jobs. To achieve this, employees must pay attention to job safety requirements and practice the safety techniques learned. This frequently means that habitual and comfortable behaviors must be eliminated or altered, while behaviors that are unfamiliar and possibly unsettling are substituted.

To reinforce desired behaviors, management must use positive and timely feedback to employees about specific behaviors and action patterns that produced desired results or achieved intended objectives.

In fact, such feedback is essential to the learning and motivation process. Positive reinforcement – such as personal recognition or performance awards – is much more effective than disciplinary action focused on eliminating unwanted behaviors. Further, the closer in time reinforcement is associated with behavior, the stronger its effect.

The feedback need not be from management. Often, the feedback within work groups prompts reinforcement of behavior change. Members of a work group that have accepted common safety improvement objectives tend to reinforce one another's behaviors through feedback. Whether or not positive change is achieved, feedback provides momentum for future accomplishment.

In order to provide feedback, management must evaluate or measure the progress of the safety objective. Measurement begins with the definition of the specified safety and health objectives and then observing specific behaviors involved. Such observation can take the form of counting the occurrences of unsafe behaviors or their by-products. To observe progress toward achieving broadly defined process improvement goals, surveys or other performance indicators may be required to examine such factors as the current level of employee involvement in safety and health activities and the effectiveness of safety and health management system processes.

Attaining commitment and involvement

Behaviors repeated and reinforced lay the foundation for personal acceptance, but employee and management commitment to and involvement in the behavior change process is critical to attain permanent performance improvement.

Employee acceptance must occur. In other words, employees must be willing to take the responsibility for paying attention to the behavior or process changes necessary to achieve specified safety and health objectives until they become part of their habitual action patterns.

A change in work habits is not attained overnight and requires continuous management support. Employees must perceive that management at all levels is behind the objectives of the safety and health system and that it supports the methods chosen to achieve them. If at all possible, the techniques used to motivate employees should blend with an organization's culture. These techniques should not be viewed as "special" or outside the management mainstream, but rather as part of the motivational methods used to achieve high levels of production and quality.

When this mesh is present, the likelihood that safety and health needs will be accommodated within the normal business function is high and, therefore, the potential for permanent improvement is increased. Motivation and behavior change techniques that do not fit in with a company's management style or are looked upon as activities outside of the mainstream are unlikely to become permanent.

The total quality management model uses attitude adjustment methods to achieve quality improvement goals in industry.

Element 8.2.1
OBM uses reinforcement and feedback to modify behavior.
Element 8.2.2
TQM uses attitude adjustment to achieve quality improvements.

Motivational models

Two models can be used to motivate employees to improve safety and health performance. One, the organization behavior management model (OBM), uses reinforcement and feedback to modify behavior. The other, the total quality management model (TQM), adjusts attitude to achieve quality improvement goals.

The models differ in terms of their efficiency in accomplishing the requirements of the three motivational variables – direction of behavior, intensity of action and persistence of effort.

Comparison of OBM vs. TQM approaches to employee motivation			
Motivational variable	Supporting action	Safety emphasis OBM model	Safety emphasis TQM model
Direction of behavior	Specify objectives	Behavior	Attitudes/behavior
	Provide training	Behavior training	Process education
Intensity of action	Give reinforcement	Behavior occurrence	Process improvement
	Maintain feedback	Behavior data	Operating indicators
Persistence of effort	Employee commitment	Behavior change	Continuous improvement
	Management commitment	Style change	Cultural change

OBM emphasizes external behavior change, while TQM emphasizes internal attitudinal changes as a prerequisite to behavior change. Accordingly, OBM objectives can probably be communicated in a more direct and simple fashion to employees, while TQM principles may be more complex and unfamiliar.

Training provided to employees through OBM and TQM differs as well. OBM training is specific in its coverage of critical behaviors to be changed, while TQM education includes behavioral as well as attitudinal skills development, such as team building and problem solving.

Both OBM and TQM models provide reinforcement and feedback, but the observational techniques used in OBM are more formal and specific to the objectives than are those used in TQM. Also, the reinforcement and feedback used in OBM are more structured than those found in TQM, thus facilitating behavior changes more rapidly.

Employee commitment to improved safety performance on a permanent basis, as reflected in both attitude and behavior changes, appears more directly attained by TQM than OBM, because of TQM's emphasis on process or root cause improvements. Process changes produced by TQM flow from employee involvement and empowerment as individuals and teams. Employees are much more likely to support change if the objectives to be achieved and the methods used to achieve them are based on their own recommendations rather than imposed by management.

OBM's emphasis on critical behaviors or special cause improvements includes some degree of employee participation in the selection of behaviors to be changed and, possibly, the incentives to be used, but control is maintained through a relatively rigid observation and reinforcement system. As a result, unless the system is continued, the permanence of the behavior change remains questionable.

With regard to management commitment, TQM requires a definite change from the philosophy that employees should be "managed" to conform to existing systems to a viewpoint that processes and systems can be improved or even completely revamped, and that employees are in the best position to know how those processes work and should work. It also calls for creation of a corporate culture featuring flexibility and responsiveness to employee needs and trust between labor and management.

The OBM approach does not demand a shift from the traditional management philosophy that seeks to manage employee behavior. It does, however, call for the acceptance of a new management style focusing on a different and relatively exacting observation system not widely used and requiring a relatively substantial amount of time and resources to maintain.

The role of motivation efforts is to support the mainline safety and health management system, not take its place. Similarly, the value of motivation techniques should not be measured by reduction in injuries, property damage or workers' compensation costs. Rather, effectiveness of motivational techniques should be judged in terms of how well they achieve their support roles. Such roles include:

- Maintaining employees' interest in their own safety
- Communicating management's interest in employee safety and health
- Generating employee involvement in safety activities
- Increasing morale and reminding employees to take special precautions

Element 8.3

Management provides visible leadership to change employee attitudes and behaviors.

Changing attitudes and behaviors

No matter how intrinsically effective a motivational model is in changing employee attitudes and behavior, ultimate success depends on visible management leadership. This is a prerequisite for any program, whether it is focused on production, product quality or employee safety and health.

Such leadership is illustrated in three main ways – through communication, through the use of incentive, reward and recognition programs, and through the implementation of employee surveys.

Communication

Communications of various kinds are used to enhance the general effectiveness of any motivational effort. Basically, the communication process is: Who says what, in which channel, to whom and with what effect? Accordingly, communication programs usually involve a source, message, media, target and objectives.

Communications vary in terms of their coverage and impact. Safety posters, banners and other mass media are high in coverage and most effective in increasing general awareness about safety and health issues and in presenting on-the-spot directions or safety reminders. They also can be a useful vehicle for making employees aware of management's general interest in their welfare.

As is the case with mass media in general, their impact is lessened when used alone because they provide no opportunity for interaction, further information or response to questions; however, the impact of their message can be increased when combined with opportunities for person-to-person or two-way communication, either through group discussions or individual contacts. Though low in coverage value, these methods can be high in impact and lead to changes in behavior.

With regard to communication content, the use of fear has been a topic of research and controversy for years. This strategy attempts to change safety and health attitudes about the risks involved in hazardous behaviors by instilling fear in a target audience and then reducing that fear by providing methods to prevent the danger or lower the risk. Workplace examples include personal protective equipment use campaigns, while non-workplace examples include anti-smoking campaigns and seat belt use programs. The main argument against using fear messages is the contention that receivers "block out" or suppress the message.

Finally, safety and health communications should consider the target group at which messages are aimed. For example, research has shown that fear messages are more effective with new employees than with seasoned employees who can use their experiences to discount the message. Additionally, fear messages have been found to be especially effective in influencing employees who are not under direct supervision and are expected to comply with safety regulations on their own.

As an aid to both defining targets and establishing objectives, employee surveys are recommended to assess current levels of safety and health knowledge, attitudes toward safety management programs and practices and compliance with rules and procedures. Such measurements assist in pinpointing education and persuasion priorities and set a baseline for later evaluations of the effectiveness of communication efforts.

Award, offer incentives, recognize

The use of incentives, awards and recognitions to motivate employees to perform safely is a feature of both OBM and TQM models. In the OBM model, use of incentives to reinforce employee behavior is critical to program success. In TQM, rewards, promotions and other incentives are used to recognize individuals for contributions to process improvement. Also, at the group, team or company level, special days or other functions are used to celebrate achievement.

Broadly speaking, the use of incentives of any type – including salary increases and promotions – can be viewed as having a positive influence on employee attitudes and behavior. When safety and health is made part of the decision to reward employee performance, these factors take on added significance as important job-related requirements.

Management should be aware, however, of the pitfalls. At the organization level, incentive or award programs for employees can be substituted for legitimate safety and health management programs. As has been indicated, motivation techniques support mainline programs, but are never a substitute for them. At the employee level, abuse can result in the failure to report an injury or incident for fear that either an individual or work group will not receive an award.

Many companies use incentives and awards as part of their safety and health system on a continuing basis.

In summary, the appropriate use of awards, incentives and recognitions can play an important helping role for organizations using them wisely.

Employee surveys

Employee surveys in the form of questionnaires and/or interviews are becoming a widely used means of uncovering safety and health management systems strengths and weaknesses. They play a critical role in TQM approaches to employee motivation, as a source of information on safety and health needs, as well as measures of performance improvement.

Surveys also stimulate employee participation in safety and health. At a minimum, a basic employee survey should consider the following five factors:

- Management leadership that clearly communicates a safety and health vision supported in words and action
- Supervisor involvement that reinforces and communicates management's vision through open employee interactions, example, training, control and recognition
- Employee responsibility that personally supports company safety and health objectives and adopts the attitudes and action necessary to achieve them
- Safety support activities that generate employee cooperation and action to achieve safety and health objectives, such as a management and non-management safety committee
- Safety support climate that sustains employees' perception that management is completely committed to employee safety and health as a top priority

Like other techniques, the benefits that can be derived from employee surveys depend on how they are used. For example, if survey results are acted on by management, they can greatly enhance employee morale and provide a strong indication that management is serious about employee safety and health. This image can be further enhanced if results are communicated to employees, at least in summary form. If, in contrast, management fails to follow up on findings, the survey activity can prove detrimental to morale and damage management's image with regard to employee safety and health.

This situation is particularly critical in organizations whose management style has been traditionally non-participative. An employee survey can be an effective way to initiate increased employee participation and to communicate this change in management style to employees; however, if there is no intention to change the prevailing management style, the use of a survey will be seen simply as "window dressing."

The primary reason for conducting an employee survey is to obtain as accurate a picture as possible of how the safety and health management system is operating. Whether or not an organization has open communications, it is frequently difficult to get an objective and balanced view of employee reactions to safety and health programs and activities. Communication barriers, whether personal on the part of individual employees or organizational in nature, can produce unbalanced impressions about program strengths as well as weaknesses.

For this reason, it is necessary to ensure all employees are given an equal opportunity to participate in a survey. This may be done by including all employees in the activity or by selecting a random sample of employees that truly represents the workplace population. If the former approach is taken, the activity takes on added morale-building value, because all employees are given an opportunity to express their opinion; however, economic considerations may preclude this possibility, particularly in large organizations. In such cases, a random sample of respondents is appropriate if the proper selection techniques are used.

It takes time, effort and resources to conduct an employee survey. Accordingly, management must be clear in how it intends to use survey findings and resolve to do whatever it takes to obtain the most objective and, therefore, most accurate and reliable results possible.

Element 8: Motivation, behavior and attitude review

Issues/questions	In place			Action plan (if "no" or "partially")
	Yes	No	Partially	
1. Are your organization's safety and health objectives stated in terms of specific behaviors and/or process improvements?				
2. Do training and education opportunities support the achievement of these objectives?				
3. Do employees receive positive reinforcement for safety and health performance/process improvement?				
4. Is safety and health integrated within your organization's management style and culture?				
5. Do communications effectively support safety and health?				
6. Are your safety and health communications prioritized?				
7. Is your communication program(s) evaluated?				
8. Is safety and health achievement recognized at the organizational level?				
9. Is safety and health achievement recognized at the employee level?				
10. Do you obtain employee input about safety and health management processes?				

9

element

training and orientation

Element 9: Training and orientation

9.1 Management plans and implements safety training to assure that a systematic and prescribed process – including needs analysis, course design and development of an evaluation strategy – is applied in a consistent manner. Safety training should include specific criteria, including:

9.1.1 Measurable and observable learning objectives that state the desired knowledge, skill or ability to be gained by the participant

9.1.2 Delivery methods – including lecture, hands-on training, demonstration, and computer-based training – that consider the background and experience of the participants and the learning objectives

9.1.3 Trainers with documented technical knowledge, skills, or abilities in the subjects they teach and with a demonstrated competence in instructional techniques and methods appropriate for adult learning

9.1.4 Trainers who are required to maintain professional competency by participating in continuing education or professional development programs related to their subject matter expertise and instructional skills

9.1.5 Training delivery that incorporates adult learning principles appropriate for the target audience and learning objectives

9.1.6 Written documentation of the evaluation methods conducted following each training session used to verify that training has achieved the desired learning objectives. Procedures should exist for assisting participants who do not achieve the learning objectives.

9.1.7 Training records maintained in accordance with the established record-keeping system

9.2 Management develops and implements an annual training plan for each operating unit. The plan should:

9.2.1 Specify the necessary competencies and technical specialty areas, the individuals responsible to serve as the technical experts and resources, and the means for those responsible to obtain necessary training, education and professional development.

9.2.2 Identify the nature of the training, dates, participants and any other special requirements. This plan should prioritize training needs and include implementation plans to accomplish the training.

9.2.3 Consider required regulatory compliance training, refresher training, management and supervisory leadership training, any specialized training needs, and safety staff and safety team professional development.

9.3 Management schedules periodic management training focusing on management's roles and responsibilities to lead the ongoing safety improvement process.

9.4 Management ensures a formal safety orientation program is provided to contractors and temporary workers prior to job assignment. The program should provide the attendee with sufficient skills and knowledge to enable them to perform their job safely. The program should include testing for comprehension and include periodic follow-ups beyond the first day by the immediate supervisor.

Overview

With knowledge growing exponentially, training and education are among the most important functions in an organization today. Information has become the commodity of the future; learning is how it is acquired.

Whether a company strives to attain superior performance through a continuous improvement model, a quality program, corporate re-engineering or any other strategy, its employees must be provided with appropriate learning opportunities. And, like quality and productivity, learning must be built into the total business process. It must become a systemic effort, not just an add-on.

Effective training programs share certain characteristics. They:
- Begin with behavioral objectives
- Build on adult learning principles
- Appeal to many learning styles
- Appeal to people from diverse cultures and experiences
- Make learning memorable and experiential
- Promote teamwork
- Use instructional design principles and phased development
- Select appropriate media

Overall, for training to be considered successful, trainees must acquire useful knowledge and skills and must apply the new knowledge and skills to their jobs and improve performance with practice and feedback.

Safety training implementation

Today, organizations must comply with myriad safety regulations – each typically with specific training requirements and standards. For example, the Occupational Safety and Health Administration (OSHA), the Mine Safety and Health Administration (MSHA) and the Environmental Protection Agency (EPA) all specify training standards in their regulations. Similarly, The European Union specifies training requirements in its Framework Directive. And the ISO 9000 – a set of universal quality system standards – requires training.

While these regulatory agencies have historically established minimum training standards, companies seeking to achieve excellence in safety and health must set corporate standards as well. To do so, management must identify workplace problems resulting from a lack of training, identify the characteristics of effective training and evaluate training programs. Training should be consistent and systematic. Further, the training process in a company must be managed, much as any other business function is managed.

Measurable objectives

Training objectives must be clearly stated. These objectives should include the desired knowledge, skill or ability to be gained by the participant. These objectives also should be measurable and observable.

Element 9.1
Management should plan and implement safety training to assure that a systematic and pre-scribed process – including needs analysis, course design and development of an evaluation strategy – is applied in a consistent manner.

Element 9.1.1
Measurable and observable learning objectives that state the desired knowledge, skill or ability to be gained by the participant

For example, new employee orientation training may include incident reporting and first aid/medical treatment procedures, hazard communication, personal protective equipment, fire protection prevention, natural disaster protection, emergency response and equipment use.

New employees can then be tested and observed to ensure understanding of the training subjects.

Delivery methods

One of the most important features of training is the opportunity to provide for people to do things with the information. In short, the more performance, the better the learning.

Some consideration of basic learning principles is valid whether the learning is in the class or in a work area. Training should be based on key principles of learning, such as reinforcement, knowledge of results, practice, meaningfulness, selective learning, frequency, recall, primacy, intensity and transfer of training.

Knowledgeable trainers

Trainers can make or break any training. Management should ensure trainers chosen have documented their technical knowledge, skills or abilities in the subject areas they will be training.

In addition, management should require trainers to demonstrate their competence in instructional techniques and methods appropriate for adult learning. A trainer who lacks basic teaching skills can undermine the entire training process.

Trainer competency

One method for ensuring a good training experience for employees is to ensure trainers' competency.

This may be accomplished by requiring trainers to participate in continuing education or professional development programs related to their expertise and instructional skills.

Adult learning principles

Taking into consideration adult learning needs is a major factor in the success of any training. To accomplish this, adult learning principles must be used in the design and delivery of training. For example, one adult learning principle is based on the belief that each person learns best through one of three senses:

- Hearing – 11 percent of humans are auditory learners
- Sight – 83 percent of humans are visual learners
- Touch or activity – 69 percent of humans are kinesthetic learners

Another adult learning principle examines the percentage of information retained based on the delivery of the information. For example, people will remember only about 10 percent of what they read.

Element 9.1.2

Delivery methods – including lecture, hands-on training, demonstration and computer-based training – that consider the background and experience of the participants and the learning objectives

Element 9.1.3

Trainers with documented technical knowledge, skills or abilities in the subjects they teach and with a demonstrated competence in instructional techniques and methods appropriate for adult learning

Element 9.1.4

Trainers who are required to maintain professional competency by participating in continuing education or professional development programs related to their subject matter expertise and instructional skills

Element 9.1.5

Training delivery that incorporates adult learning principles appropriate for the target audience and learning objectives

These adult learning principles are critical to any training program development. These should be considered along with the type of audience being trained, such as supervisors or employees.

People remember	Of what they
10%	Read
20%	Hear
30%	See
50%	Hear and See
70%	Say
90%	Say and Do

Training documentation

Training is expensive – in terms of time, resources and dollars. Therefore, it is critical for management to evaluate the effectiveness of the training and measure the return on investment. The evaluation methods used to determine if training is achieving its goal must be documented. Four levels of evaluation will provide management with measurements of the effectiveness of the training.

- **Participant reaction:** Examine participants' reaction to training through the use of anonymous questionnaires at the end of a program.
- **Classroom assessment:** Analyze knowledge gained by participants through the use of pre- and post-tests based on behavioral objectives.
- **On-the-job assessment:** Observe participants' performance through the use of self-reports of skill improvements and proficiency tests to measure the on-the-job skills developed by the training.
- **Organization improvement:** Calculate the effects of the training by looking at changes in incidents and injury rates.

Record maintenance

Regulatory agencies and quality assurance programs have increased the emphasis on record keeping. For this reason, it is critical that management maintain training records using established record-keeping systems – complete with a written policy identifying who is allowed to access training records and under what conditions.

Historically, employers have kept training information – such as training programs attended, dates of training, location of training and purpose of training – within the standard employee records. Today, additional data may need to be kept. For example, it may be necessary also to maintain data about the method of evaluation, evaluation scores, training methods and instructors.

In addition to meeting stricter regulatory requirements, record keeping serves other purposes. For example, data can be used in a lawsuit to demonstrate company commitment to training. Data pertaining to the effectiveness and costs of past training programs could be used as a tool for planning future training budgets.

Annual training plan

Management should develop a written statement about the organization's policy on training, as well as for each operating unit. The policy should define training programs for all levels of management and employees. It should reinforce the principle that safety training is good business and can actually improve production and performance rather than interfere with it. A strong policy will help a company fulfill its safety and health missions and regulatory and legal obligations.

In addition to policy, management must establish training budgets. To budget, consider costs of training, including:

- Course materials, whether purchased or developed in house
- Physical space and equipment needed
- Trainers, administration to coordinate training and maintain records
- Employee salaries
- Outside training fees
- Other employee costs, such as transportation, meals and lodging

Technical expertise

As part of the annual training plan, management must specify areas of training, technical experts and resources and additional training or professional development needed by those responsible for training.

To determine areas of training, management should systematically examine loss exposures. The goal of training would be to reduce hazards posing threats to employee safety. It also is important to consider the qualifications required of the people who will develop or teach training, and to keep those qualifications up to date.

Training specifics

Decisions must be made regarding participants and the training. Examine risks to different employee groups and set priorities. Company injury and illness data can provide historical information. Examining work procedures can prevent future incidents from occurring and is a forward-looking approach to determining training needs. In addition, it is usually necessary to identify training taken by specific employees.

Making time for training is a difficult task in most companies. Schedule training so it does not greatly interfere with production demands and notify employees in advance. Also, allow time for follow-up practice, coaching and other activities.

Management must consider all of the various types of training – including training originating from manufacturer equipment recommendations or training required by government agencies.

Element 9.2

Management should develop and implement an annual training plan for each operating unit.

Element 9.2.1

Specify the necessary competencies and technical specialty areas, the individuals responsible to serve as the technical experts and resources, and the means for those responsible to obtain necessary training, education and professional development.

Element 9.2.2

Identify the nature of the training, dates, participants and any other special requirements. This plan should prioritize training needs and include implementation plans to accomplish the training.

161

Element 9.2.3

Consider required regulatory compliance training, refresher training, management and supervisory leadership training, any specialized training needs and safety staff and safety team professional development.

Regulatory training

In the United States, companies are responsible for knowing which federal, state and local regulations apply to their business. Many regulations specify training standards or training performance.

While there are many regulatory agencies at the federal level, three of the most important ones for safety and health in business and industry are OSHA, MSHA, and EPA.

Among the OSHA regulations that require training are hazard communication, bloodborne pathogens, hearing conservation, powder-actuated tools, asbestos regulations, forklift tractor operations, process safety management, fire and emergency rescue and first aid/CPR. Some regulations, such as OSHA's Electrical Safety-Related Work Practices Regulation, specify who must be trained, where training can take place and the kind of training required for different types of workers.

Element 9.3

Management should schedule periodic management training, focusing on management's roles and responsibilities to lead the ongoing safety improvement process.

Management training

Safety management training is directed at senior management for the basic reason that "change begins at the top." Safety and health programs for management should contain information about setting safety and health goals, measuring the effectiveness of achieving those goals and outlining the types of programs needed to achieve them.

In addition, management training should include information about the processes used to implement a safety and health system. These processes will help identify management's roles and responsibilities in the continuous safety process. Processes should include:

- Collecting and analyzing company data. The data must be factual, accurate, credible, concise, comparative and in the language of finance.
- Creating a vision for the company's performance in safety and health and integrating it with other business issues, like quality.
- Communicating both upstream and downstream. To communicate effectively, build credibility, present solutions to problems and follow company protocol.

Element 9.4

Management should ensure a formal safety orientation program is provided to contractors and temporary workers prior to job assignment. The program should provide the attendee with sufficient skills and knowledge to enable them to perform their job safely. The program should include testing for comprehension and periodic follow-up by the immediate supervisor beyond the first day.

Contractor training

In addition to safety and health training for employees, businesses also must provide training for outside workers brought on-site for contract or temporary work. Before any work begins, the employer should meet with contractor management and safety staff to conduct a safety orientation program. Such a program should include worksite safety and training requirements.

Similar to employee safety and health training, a training program for contract or temporary workers should provide information about the skills and knowledge needed to perform their jobs safely. Further, the training should include testing for comprehension and periodic follow-up.

Element 9: Training and orientation review

Issues/questions	In place			Action plan (if "no" or "partially")
	Yes	No	Partially	
1. Do policy statements and practices support your company as a "learning organization"?				
2. Is the management team kept well informed of United States and international regulations that apply to the company and specify training?				
3. Do training standards and controls ensure acquisition and application of training topics?				
4. Are training outcomes evaluated?				
5. Is the training process managed with budgets, schedules, records, value, etc.?				
6. Are safety and health programs provided for management?				
7. Is there a formal training process for temporary or contract workers?				

appendix

Element 1: Management leadership and commitment

1.1 Executive management is ultimately responsible for leading the safety improvement process and for ensuring all levels of line management implement the safety management system.

1.2 Executive management maintains a clearly stated safety and health policy and clearly communicates it to all employees.

1.3 Executive management creates clear safety program goals as well as corresponding objectives designed to meet those goals.

1.4 Executive management maintains a safety performance measurement and monitoring system including proactive performance measures for individuals at all levels of the organization.

1.5 Executive management shows visible participation and involvement on a regular basis in a variety of planned and proactive safety activities.

1.6 Executive management assigns responsibilities, roles and commensurate authority to managers and supervisors. They also provide assistance and training to support employee understanding of and capability to perform these roles.

1.7 Executive management allocates sufficient resources to support achievement of program goals and objectives.

1.8 Executive management uses a system of accountability to ensure managers, supervisors and employees accomplish their assigned safety responsibilities.

1.9 Executive management requires periodic reviews of programs, projects and activities to determine their effectiveness in achieving goals and objectives.

1.10 Executive management makes safety performance a key indicator of organizational excellence and integrates it into the business planning process.

Element 2: Organizational communications and system documentation

2.1 Management establishes and maintains policies for communicating information about the safety management system. They include methods for conveying, documenting and responding to both internal and external communications.

2.2 Management has a mechanism for communicating safety and health information from the top leadership, through all levels of management and supervision, to employees.

2.3 Management maintains a mechanism for getting feedback from employees to the appropriate level of management, including senior management.

2.4 Management maintains a record-keeping system that includes a clearly written document control procedure. This system identifies:

  2.4.1 Who has access to and responsibility for maintaining the record-keeping and document-control system

  2.4.2 What documents, records or other pertinent data the system should maintain (documents should be retrievable, readily identifiable, legible and dated)

  2.4.3 How long the system will maintain the records and how the system will keep documents up-to-date

  2.4.4 Where records are located and how people can access them.

2.5 The record-keeping documents generate information enabling the organization to evaluate safety performance and make improvements. This information includes the following:

  2.5.1 Injury and illness data, including off-the-job injury data and related costs

  2.5.2 Data from incident investigations

  2.5.3 Industrial hygiene surveys and exposure monitoring results

  2.5.4 Results of (as well as status of corrective action from) safety performance reviews, management assessments, third party audits and inspections

  2.5.5 Safety policy, procedures, safe work practices, program objectives and goal status

  2.5.6 Roles and responsibilities for program areas

  2.5.7 Process safety reviews, risk assessments and hazard analysis

  2.5.8 Elements of the safety management system and their connection to each other

Element 3: Assessments, audits and continuous improvement

3.1 Management periodically conducts safety management system assessments to learn the effectiveness of the current system, identify and prioritize areas of improvement and propose changes to enhance the safety management system. They ensure the results are documented and entered into the occupational safety and health record-keeping system.

3.2 Management establishes formal policy and procedures for periodic audits. The business plan and the organization's safety and health priorities drive the design for the audit system, which is preventive in nature and focuses on audits that are most likely to expose hazards and unsafe conditions. Employees at all levels of the organization participate and give input into the development of the audit system. The final system includes the following components.

3.2.1 A summary of the types of audits that should be conducted

3.2.2 The scope and purpose of each audit

3.2.3 Defined roles, responsibilities, qualifications and competencies of team members

3.2.4 A schedule for the various types of audits

3.2.5 Standards and procedures for conducting the audits

3.2.6 Observations, findings and management response

3.2.7 A program review of one or all of the elements of the safety management system

3.3 The safety management system is based on the principles of continuous improvement, which include the following:

3.3.1 Management commitment to and leadership of the continuous improvement process

3.3.2 Assessing the current situation and identifying the issues using the nine elements as a guide

3.3.3 Planning measurable improvement goals, strategies and tactics

3.3.4 Implementing these plans

3.3.5 Reviewing and adjusting the process to facilitate constant improvement

Element 4: Hazard recognition, evaluation and control

4.1 Management establishes and maintains a policy for ongoing recognition, evaluation and control or elimination of workplace hazards in order to maintain an acceptable level of risk in the workplace. The hazard control policy should establish:

4.1.1 Written procedures to be used in identifying, analyzing and controlling hazards

4.1.2 A budget with sufficient funds for effective hazard control program implementation

4.1.3 The active involvement and participation of workers exposed to hazards as an essential element of the hazard control program

4.1.4 A reliable system that encourages employees to report hazards and concerns and that includes a method to follow up with employees

4.2 Management establishes a hazard analysis procedure to identify existing and potential hazards, as well as conditions and operations in which changes might create hazards. Several tools may be used to do this based on organizational needs, capabilities and resources. These include job safety analysis, safety inspections, risk assessments, industrial hygiene exposure assessments, incident investigations, process hazard analysis and system safety reviews. To implement a thorough analysis:

4.2.1 Conduct a comprehensive, baseline survey for safety and health and periodic, comprehensive update surveys. Areas to be considered within the survey include: environment, including chemical, physical, biological and ergonomic hazards, as well as walking/working surfaces, lighting, temperature and ventilation; equipment and processes, including construction plans, tool/equipment conditions, housekeeping, and machine and electrical safeguards; and employee/management work practices, including use of personal protective equipment, appropriate equipment, tools and machines, safety devices, established safe work practices and proper lifting techniques.

4.2.2 Perform routine job hazard analysis.

4.2.3 Conduct periodic and daily safety and health inspections of the workplace.

4.2.4 Include a change analysis of planned and new facilities, processes, materials, and equipment or when staffing changes occur.

4.2.5 Review hazards found during worksite analysis to determine the safety system failure that caused the hazard. The system failure should then be corrected to ensure similar hazards do not reoccur.

4.2.6 Document analysis results and enter into the record-keeping system.

4.3 Management will initiate a hazard evaluation or risk assessment process. The hazard evaluation system will assess risks according to probability of occurrences, severity of outcomes and employee exposure. The qualitative hazard probability should be determined through research, analysis and evaluation of historical safety data on similar systems.

4.3.1 Establish appropriate definitions of hazard severity, probability and exposure categories to establish understandable qualitative measures for incidents that might occur if a potential hazard is identified.

4.4 Management will insure staff design and implement control measures when worker exposure to health or physical hazards is found to pose an unacceptable risk. The best practice approach is to eliminate hazards at the design stage. If not feasible, the following hierarchy of control measures should be applied:

4.4.1 Engineering controls should be used as the first and most reliable strategy to control a hazard at its source when workers are exposed to hazards.

4.4.2 Administrative controls can be used to minimize worker exposure through policies, procedures and rules such as standard operating procedures when engineering controls are not feasible.

4.4.3 Personal protective equipment can be used as a supplementary control method when exposure to hazards cannot be engineered out of the process and when administrative controls cannot provide sufficient protection. Use PPE when engineering and administrative controls are not feasible, as an interim control method while "higher" controls are being implemented or as added protection. PPE should not be used as a substitute for engineering or administrative controls.

Element 5: Workplace design and engineering

5.1 Management establishes a policy and procedures to ensure a design and start-up review process will be applied for all new or redesigned equipment and process systems. In implementing this policy, management will establish well-defined objectives, assess hazard probability and severity, establish design review procedures and use project checklists. The policy will establish minimum requirements and set responsibility and accountability when conducting design reviews. Design standards will be established for the following:

5.1.1 Facility layout, workstation and machine design

5.1.2 Relevant safety and health regulations and standards

5.1.3 The relationship between the worker and the job (ergonomic design considerations)

5.1.4 Proper material handling including both mechanical and manual handling

5.1.5 The safety and health aspects of automated processes

5.1.6 Life safety and fire protection

Element 6: Operational safety and health programs

6.1 Management establishes compliance policies for mandatory occupational safety programs based on regulations, as well as voluntary safety management system goals based on the needs of the organization. The regulatory compliance policy should:

6.1.1 Set forth written procedures to be used in determining the applicability of government mandated standards.

6.1.2 Direct staff to identify and implement best safety practices in applying a safety management system to the workplace.

6.1.3 Insure sufficient funds are budgeted for the implementation and ongoing needs of standards.

6.1.4 Clearly define roles, responsibilities, expectations and accountability for compliance by all employees.

6.2 Management must determine the scope and nature of the organization's occupational health program and allocate resources to provide appropriate service. Management should develop program goals and establish functions, programs, procedures and activities to meet the organizations health goals. At a minimum, the health program should:

6.2.1 Prevent occupational illnesses through control of risk factors

6.2.2 Ensure proper treatment of work-related illnesses and injuries

6.3 Management must determine the scope and nature of the organization's occupational safety program and allocate resources to provide appropriate services. Management should develop program goals and establish functions, programs, procedures and activities to meet the organization's occupational safety goals. The two goals of an occupational safety program should be:

6.3.1 To implement all safety programs required by mandatory standards

6.3.2 To institute "best safety practices" and a proactive safety management system designed to prevent employee injuries

6.4 Management establishes policies and procedures for the effective management and control of external exposures. External exposures include any influences or risks that arise outside the boundaries of the company property or are caused by a third party. Five major types of external exposures include:

6.4.1 Natural disasters

6.4.2 Contract employees

6.4.3 Vendors

6.4.4 Products produced by the company

6.4.5 Public liability

Element 7: Employee involvement

7.1 Management has a policy or other documents that identify employee involvement as an element vital to the success of a safety management system. The documentation identifies specific employee involvement goals, activities and benefits that the organization expects to derive from those activities.

7.1.1 The organization has identified benefits expected from employee involvement activities.

7.1.2 The organization has identified specific goals for levels of employee involvement. The goal may be a specified number of employees, a specified number of activities or implementation of actions identified as gaps through the assessment process.

7.2 Management has a policy or other documents that identify site-specific employee involvement tools used in its safety management system. Included are the following elements:

7.2.1 Individual development and training

7.2.2 Individual involvement and influence

7.2.3 Constant and varied communication

7.2.4 At-risk behavior auditing

7.2.5 Recognition and reward

7.2.6 Appropriate hazard recognition tools such as:

7.2.6.1 Job safety analysis

7.2.6.2 Physical hazard inspections

7.2.6.3 Employee safety training

7.2.6.4 Safety meetings

7.2.6.5 Job safety observations

7.2.6.6 Safety committees or teams

Element 8: Motivation, behavior and attitudes

8.1 Management uses motivation to change employee behavior and attitudes. Motivation is defined by three variables:

8.1.1 Direction of behavior

8.1.2 Intensity of action

8.1.3 Persistence of effort

8.2 Management uses motivational approaches to improve safety and health performance.

8.2.1 The organization behavior management model uses reinforcement and feedback to modify behavior.

8.2.2 The total quality management model uses attitude adjustment methods to achieve quality improvement goals in industry.

8.3 Management provides visible leadership to change employee attitudes and behaviors.

Element 9: Training and orientation

9.1 Management should plan and implement safety training to assure that a systematic and prescribed process – including needs analysis, course design and development of an evaluation strategy – is applied in a consistent manner. Safety training should include specific criteria, including:

9.1.1 Measurable and observable learning objectives that state the desired knowledge, skill or ability to be gained by the participant

9.1.2 Delivery methods – including lecture, hands-on training, demonstration and computer-based training – that consider the background and experience of the participants and the learning objectives.

9.1.3 Trainers with documented technical knowledge, skills, or abilities in the subjects they teach and with a demonstrated competence in instructional techniques and methods appropriate for adult learning

9.1.4 Trainers who are required to maintain professional competency by participating in continuing education or professional development programs related to their subject matter expertise and instructional skills

9.1.5 Training delivery that incorporates adult learning principles appropriate for the target audience and learning objectives

9.1.6 Written documentation of the evaluation methods conducted following each training session used to verify that training has achieved the desired learning objectives. Procedures should exist for assisting participants who do not achieve the learning objectives.

9.1.7 Training records maintained in accordance with the established record-keeping system

9.2 Management should develop and implement an annual training plan for each operating unit. The plan should:

9.2.1. Specify the necessary competencies and technical specialty areas, the individuals responsible to serve as the technical expert and resource, and the means for those responsible to obtain necessary training, education and professional development

9.2.2 Identify the nature of the training, dates, participants and any other special requirements. This plan should prioritize training needs and include implementation plans to accomplish the training.

9.2.3 Consider required regulatory compliance training, refresher training, management and supervisory leadership training, any specialized training needs, and safety staff and safety team professional development.

9.3 Management should schedule periodic management training focusing on management's roles and responsibilities to lead the ongoing safety improvement process.

9.4 Management should ensure a formal safety orientation program is provided to contractors and temporary workers prior to job assignment. The program should provide the attendee with sufficient skills and knowledge to enable them to perform their job safely. The program should include testing for comprehension and include periodic follow-up beyond first day by the immediate supervisor.

index